D1281817

Also by William Demby

BEETLECREEK

THE CATACOMBS

Pantheon Books

A DIVISION OF RANDOM HOUSE

New York

THE
CATACOMBS

William Demby

FIRST PRINTING

© *Copyright, 1965, by William Demby*

All rights reserved under International and Pan-American
Copyright Conventions. Published in New York by Pantheon
Books, a division of Random House, Inc., and simultaneously
in Toronto, Canada, by Random House of Canada Limited.
Manufactured in the United States of America by The Haddon
Craftsmen, Scranton, Pa.

Library of Congress catalog card number: 64-18343

DESIGN BY TERE LOPRETE

For Tatina

THE CATACOMBS

I

This is a day in March. Here in Rome it is nine o'clock in the morning. The sun has finally come out and my Rotella collages have begun to dance like gorgeous jungle flowers. I sit here at my desk waiting for Doris to come. With her approval I am writing a novel about her. I know that she has spent the night with the Count, and I am waiting for her to come tell me all about it in detail. In the meantime, I read my newspapers—five from

Rome, one each from Turin and Milan. Other people collect stamps or matchboxes, or raise chinchillas, or invent games based upon Euclidean logic. I see no reason, then, why some of my friends find it eccentric, or a waste of valuable time (time, always time, and who among us knows what time, always time, really is?) that I experience so much pleasure in reading some fourteen or fifteen Italian newspapers and magazines every day. Reading my newspapers, relishing (gourmand of the printed word) the immaculate virginity of the crisp almost white paper and the urgent seduction of adventure in the smoky anthracite smell of the ink, analyzing even the most minute (but human) event, linking it to the blaring rhetorical headlines of several days before, recalling some insignificant item reprinted from a provincial newspaper months and months before—no, I feel not like God, but rather like some benevolently mad theatrical impresario who eagerly, paternally, leafs through the press clippings of his countless actors and actresses, dispersed monads, who like nomads are wandering over the theatrical caravan routes of the world. No: I do not gain pleasure from stamps, from matchboxes, from chinchillas, from the invention of games—my warmest, most secretly perverse pleasure comes from observing (and vicariously participating in—alas, my trade is that of a writer) the seeming mutations, the illusory motion, the dreamlike sense of progression and progress which occur when the sun's ray shifts on the eternal and timeless, the static, the sacredly silk-threaded tapestry of lives . . .

I stop to write a long overdue letter to a friend in Alabama, who has sent me a play of hers to read: Dear Trudy, I have purposely waited writing to you until I was truly convinced of what I am about to say. You are in crisis. Most sensitive people today are in crisis. But as a writer, a born writer (or perhaps better, a born poetess), your crisis is reflected in your writing. This play of yours does not interest me very much—nor does it really interest you very much. Were you seriously interested in the problems of school desegregation, you would have taken a more active part in the dramatic developments in your town last year. These are not problems you are truly interested in (I wrote a novel about the same things last winter: it too rang false, and I gave the MS to Gigi, the neighborhood junkman). Remember your poem about the Hollyhocks? Already then (you were only eleven years old) it was obvious to all that you were an authentic poetess . . . my suggestion then is that through short, *intense*, profoundly intense, poems you talk about yourself and the crisis you are going through (and believe me, your crisis is by no means unique—I am just now beginning to get out of my crisis by writing another novel, this one important slow and good!). Strangely, you are in an enviable position to touch the fundamental key to your crisis and the crisis of young people and young poets everywhere. I hope you will think seriously about this. At first write very short poems (I will be glad to try to place them in one of the reviews published here or in Paris), poems which crystallize your unique experience (Donald gazing blankly at the TV screen in the evening after hours and hours at the hospital touching with his own hands the wet messy wounds of concrete human suffering: how does he manage—one doctor for over ten thousand Negroes? The boat anchored in the river only after a special law was passed in the county seat). Urgently, you must try to touch *reality*, the reality of your own rich and unique experience. Remember, you are a poetess, and I think possibly a great one. Later, you shall try the theatre again, or perhaps a novel. Pull yourself together, then get well. (Do not worry about the obscenities which instinctively come to your lips after a drink or so too much. Obscenities are after all words, poetic words: they do no real harm, but in their magical connotations are better used in poetry. Actually, I found you in fine and sharp intellectual form when we met in New York this fall; I am sure Donald is too. By the way, has he ever thought of doing wild way-out *New Yorker*-type cartoons on some of the more grotesque aspects of being a Negro doctor in a small Alabama town, or about the "Race Problem"? I am sure they would be very saleable: I still remember the cartoons he drew to illustrate his med school yearbook.) My blessing to you all, and especially to gold-minted precious Mammy Starr. Much love, William.

The doorbell rings. This must be Doris at last. I hastily fold the letter. I pause a moment until my heart stops pounding (I wonder if I am falling in love with

(*6*)

Doris and, if so, whether this will harm or enhance the novel I am writing about her). I open the door. It is the mailman—an invitation from the United States Information Service here in Rome to attend a lecture being given by Fernanda Pivana Sottsass (she is the Italian translator of my first novel, *Beetlecreek*) on "The White Whale and Other Myths," a postcard from Harold Engels, who is vacationing on Procida, and an invitation to the opening of Giulio Turcato's show at the Tartaruga Gallery (the presentation by the poet Emilio Villa begins: "The laborious hands of Ulysses become skinned on the sharp rocks and leave tiny shreds of epidermis . . .")

I return to my table and gaze moodily at the disorderly array of newspapers. I pick up *Il Giorno* and see that there is another excerpt from N.C.'s "Algerian Diary." N. is a young aristocrat whom I first met five years ago in Positano. I was not particularly impressed with him then. He seemed soft and indolent, somehow spiritually dehydrated, my idea of a typical decadent Italian aristocrat (for some reason, ever since childhood when my brother and I built a model of the Coronation Coach from plans in the Sunday comic section of the *Pittsburgh Sun-Telegraph*, I have been obsessed with aristocrats; even today I eagerly read every scrap of news I can get my hands on about Princess Margaret, for whom I have had a secret passion ever since I was twelve years old).

Yet here he is today a national hero, having displayed

rare courage in defying the European Secret Army's order for all Italian journalists to leave Algeria or face certain death. The other Italian journalists left Algeria twenty-four hours after the ultimatum. N. has just returned to Italy after three days of hiding in the Casbah. Last night I saw him on television. Even this brief appearance must have required great courage, since one of the correspondents for the Italian Radio-TV network, who in a special TV interview reported on his harrowing experience, was threatened by Secret Army agents here in Rome, who up to now have been operating with disconcerting freedom. N. seemed to have aged, he seemed genuinely frightened, which makes the courage he displayed all the more remarkable (but who knows of what mysterious chemistry the fabric of courage is woven). But his slender pale hands lay with calm limpness on his knees as he described the unbelievable chaos that reigns on the corpse-littered streets of Algeria, and I remember asking myself whether the calm repose of his hands was due to his aristocratic breeding or to tranquillizer drugs . . .

"Monday, March 5," the excerpt from his diary begins. "Early this morning, shortly after four, I am awakened by a series of explosions. I count about thirty of them, and then give up counting. Some of the explosions are faint and distant; others, though, are so near and violent that the windows in my room rattle. The explosions continue for almost two hours. It is as if Algeria is being bombed. Shortly after the sound of explosions in the night, there comes another sound: the screaming of police sirens and the sirens of ambulances speeding through the streets . . ."

Suddenly sick of the world, sick of the poisonous potion of anxiety and anguish filtered through row after monotonous row of identical typeface, I pick up my copy of Viking Press's *Portable Walt Whitman* and read from his Civil War Diary: ". . . The night was very pleasant, at times the moon shining out full and clear, all Nature so calm in itself, the early summer grass so rich, and foliage of the trees—yet there the battle raging, and many good fellows lying helpless, with no accessions to them, and every minute amid the rattle of muskets and crash of cannon (for there was an artillery contest too, the red life-blood oozing out from heads or trunks or limbs upon that green and dew-cool grass). Patches of woods take fire, and several of the wounded, unable to move, are consumed—quite large spaces are swept over, burning the dead also—some of the men have their hair and beards singed—others holes burnt in their clothing. The flames of fire from the cannon, the quick flaring flames and smoke, and the immense roar—the musketry so general, the light nearly bright enough for each side to see the other—the crashing, tramping of men—the yelling—close quarters—we hear the secesh yells—our men cheer loudly back, especially if Hooker is in sight—hand-to-hand conflicts, each side stands up to it, brave, determined as demons, they often charge upon us—a thousand deeds are done worth newer, greater poems on—and still the woods on fire—still many not only scorch'd—too many, unable to move, are burn'd to death . . ."

I put down the book. The room becomes so quiet, so still, that I seem to float, backward and forward in time. The American Civil War, the Algerian War. Plastic bombs! The cheap anonymous weapon of cheap anonymous killers. The renegade officers of the European Secret Army who call their bargain-basement terrorism, their cowardly bargain basement heroics, "revolutionary warfare." But what revolution can ever succeed based on the traumatic use of psychological terror? Is it not time for the Crusades to come to an end? In this sunrise age of atomic energy the psychopathic descendants of the paladins, the mystical (and greedy) Knight Templars, have abandoned the sword and the certainty of faith for the underworld certainty of darkness—for the riskless anonymity of the plastic bomb!

But, I ask, is such riskless anonymous terrorism really effective as a political instrument?

I doubt it. For plastic bombs are cheap, are as available to all as the installment purchase of a television set (today even an oil-rich Arabian sheik can afford the price of an atomic bomb, so available have the arms of destruction become in this cruel and Gothic year 1962!); suddenly all of us can be terrorists—a young woman, verging on insanity because of disillusionment in love, drops a poisonous pill in a metropolis' milk supply center; a thrill-seeking youth, nourished on cheap intoxicating drugs and comic books, surreptitiously drops a powder in the fuel tank of a proud Boeing 707 Intercontinental Jet; anarchy, guerilla warfare spread floodlike from the fields of battle to the urban centers; no one is safe; the unspoken unwritten code of mutual trust upon which our increasingly complicated society depends has been violated; no longer is there an island-protected power elite to stand by aloof and immune; no one is safe; mad dogs roam the streets; the plague year is here; a disgruntled unemployed electrician, angry with the light company for cutting off his electricity, secretly cuts a wire and the elevators of a great skyscraper in New York come to a halt between the sixty-third and sixty-fourth floors; the plague year is here, only the God of Light and Reason, the God of Misericordia and Brotherly Love can save us. Amen . . .

At last she has come! Doris bursts into the room like an explosion of sunflowers. As always, her astonishing nightclub-dancing vitality intimidates me. Always during these unpredictable visits of hers to my studio I become almost ashamed to be a writer. In her stormy fresh-minted presence, my soul shrivels and becomes clerklike and shabby. My writer's mask slips down over my neck and the grimly smiling skull of a certified accountant is revealed. When Doris comes, the atomic balance of my dusty book-lined studio is upset: my inner ear hears the crackling of minute magnetic explosions, my inner eye sees colorless flames shimmering around her body. Then it is that I am suddenly filled with an almost overwhelming desire (ancestral?) to escape the uncomfortable present and take to the forest (how much memory, how many billions of years of ancestral memory, can the human machine endure before vital action becomes imperative?), take to the forest and hunt and be hunted, abandon this dusty cowardly retreat, abandon the typeface and the sterile and deathly purity of paper, take to the forest and hunt and be hunted, and let history rest in peace, let history remain unwritten and unrecorded, let history (man's feeble scratching on the eternally shifting sands of the desert) ferment and through the never-to-be-solved mystery of memory at long last (alchemy of sacred wine) free and intoxicate the imprisoned human mind . . .

Doris laughs and the dust particles giving aural substance to the sun's rays churn and mill about like a storm of migrating birds. She tosses her shawl on my table, a newspaper falls to the floor, she plops down on my cracked leather armchair and crosses her long, forest-tapered legs. Doris says (as magically the ray of the morning sun shifts from my Rotella collages and spotlights now the subtle roundness of her chaste hips in repose): "Oh, these Italians! These Italian men! I tell you, no kidding, the world's going to the dogs! If they ever decide to drop Big Daddy's Bomb, it's all the fault of these Latin lovers, it's all the fault of these Italian men . . . !"

Alert, my forefinger nervously beating out a tom-tom rhythm on my table, I say: "Doris, you're drunk, and at this time of the morning!" My heart has begun to pound uncontrollably again and my voice rises shrilly as I add: "You spent the night with the Count, didn't you?...Tell me about it—did something go wrong?"

Aggressively Doris snatches a cigarette from her silver cigarette case; it is as if she is unsheathing a sword for a duel: "Did something go wrong, the professor wants to know!" she says, cruelly mimicking what already I realize had been a condescending, oh-so-understanding, writer-interviewer's tone of voice. At the same time her Cleopatra's eyes blaze furiously (Doris is one of Elizabeth Taylor's handmaidens in Twentieth Century-Fox's Cleopatra colossal now being filmed in Rome and, though on several occasions I have tried to persuade her not to, she insists on wearing the grotesquely exotic— but I must admit, for her, strangely appropriate— make-up she wears before the cameras; her hairdo, too, is authentically ancient Egyptian—a back-leaning cone which somehow makes me think of a black lacquered cone of spider webs, a magical fertility symbol floating detachedly over the masklike beauty of her enchanted, nut-brown monkey face . . .).

"Did something go wrong, the professor wants to know!" she repeats, blowing out a fierce blast of smoke. "I'll say something went wrong! Something went worse than wrong! And now that we're on the subject, I'll tell you something else! I don't appreciate it one bit, your introducing me to that phony sonuvabitch. Count or no Count—I don't ever want to see him again as long as I live!"

II

. . . But now today is yesterday, and a cold dismal rain falls upon the ancient paving stones outside the country trattoria where Doris and the Count are eating in silence. There are no other customers in the small one-room restaurant. The clinking of knife and fork against plate is amplified in the mummified quiet generated by the rain. The entrance to the Catacombs is just across the Appian Way; Doris and the Count have come to the restaurant

—though it is only 5:00 P.M., two hours before normal opening time—when it began to rain after their visit to the martyrs' graves. Slowly, almost sacramentally, Doris lifts her glass of wine and drinks; her gaze turns inward. She is thinking: "Rome is beginning to give me the creeps, all this antiquity, all this piling up dead things and dead people on top of each other, those Catacombs damn sure gave me the creeps, the way that Irish priest cracked jokes and played with those bones; saints or no saints, I just don't like . . . I just don't think it's right . . . there's something spooky and weird about . . . I don't like no graveyard where you have to pay to see dead peoples' bones . . . "

The Count dabs primly at his thin lips and smiles. He turns slightly and looks out the window. In this moment the late afternoon sun probes feebly through the low rain clouds sluggishly migrating toward the airport, and at once the ancient paving stones of the Appian Way begin to bloom through the fine tinsled drizzle, like a disorderly array of unhatched dinosaur eggs.

Raffaele is a count and looks like a count. He is thirty years old, vigorous of forehead and gesture, he has a broad, well-sculptured nose, small constantly amused and curious eyes, the pupils gray but speckled with gold, and a calm, almost detached, expression on his face which mirrors an inner security anchored solidly in social position and wealth. He dresses like a junior executive in a Manhattan advertising agency, but the cut of his silk shirt is Italian, and he proudly wears the striped tie of an English public school. Raffaele's smile becomes broader: he is about to say something but is waiting cautiously until the correct English words line up paradelike in his mind. Finally the phrase forming in his mind stands at attention. But before he can open his mouth the waiter rushes over to the table to pick up the lipstick-smeared napkin Doris has just dropped on the floor . . .

Raffaele is annoyed and impatient, for the waiter lingers at the table to fill Doris' glass from the green bottle of Soave that reigns slenderly over the midmeal disorder on the table. Instinctively Doris arranges her gold-embroidered shawl around her almost bare shoulders and smiles up at the waiter. The waiter is a darkly handsome youth with absurdly classical features but with the heavy capable hands and grimy fingernails of an automobile mechanic. Now as the waiter shuffles off to his post near the fireplace, in which a pile of kindling wood and crumpled newspapers stands unlighted, Raffaele smiles across the table at Doris. Doris smiles back at him, then turns her attention back to her plate. Her fork movements as she eats the tiny slivers of dark pheasant flesh which laboriously she manages to separate from the breastbone are cautious, stagy. She seems tense, nervous, and for a moment she and the Count chew in unison like twin ventriloquist dummies. Finally Raffaele clears his throat and says (he works for a British airline ticket office in Rome, public relations, and his accent is the melodious tight-lipped accent of an Italian count who has studied in England and now works for a British airline office in Rome): "Why so pensive? Is something bothering you? You *are* free this afternoon, aren't you?"

Doris raises her eyebrows and assumes a comical air of innocence: "Oh, was I pensive? I wasn't aware of being particularly pensive. I thought I was being composed— *decomposed!*" She breaks out laughing, and somehow her dream-secret Negro laughter seems sacrilegious here in this country trattoria on the ancient Appian Way, and the Catacombs with their layers and layers of bone-powder death just across the street. "What I mean is—if you really had to take me sightseeing—and the good Lord knows I have enough sightseeing to my credit to have earned at least five Mortician degrees—why bring me to the Catacombs? Isn't there anything else to see in Rome except churches and tombs?"

"I had my reasons. But to get back to what we were saying a few minutes ago—wherever did you get such a preposterous idea? Why, there must be thousands, perhaps even millions, of Italians who are blond, blonder even than me . . . than I . . ."

"Than me . . . than I . . ." Doris says, giggling.

She is getting slightly drunk from the wine and defiantly she straightens her shoulders. "Than me . . . me is the object of what . . . or than . . . I am . . . the subject of—?"

The Count nervously shifts his weight on the hard seat of the chair. Doris grasps the neck of the bottle and unsteadily fills her glass again. She starts to fill the

Count's glass. Almost too abruptly he claps his hand over the glass and says: "Not for me, thank you. I've had enough . . ." But as soon as the words have crossed his lips, he realizes that Doris is offended. Desperately he tries to think of something to say that will mitigate the implied reproach of his tone. As he forces a smile and reaches for the bottle, and pours himself another glass of the cool pale wine, and drinks it energetically, a man among men, an aristocrat drinking with his serfs, discussing football on a rainy Sunday afternoon, he cannot help noting that Doris has withdrawn inside herself again. The agitated field of telepathic energy separating their faces warns him that she is thinking violent thoughts . . .

He's trying to make me, Doris is thinking, as once again the Count begins to dab primly at his thin lips and smiles into her eyes—as absently he brushes bread crumbs off the stylishly narrow lapel of his expensive flannel blazer—and do you know something, girl, after those spooky Catacombs, now why do you think he wanted to take me there? Why, hell, you could get lost down there, saints and martyrs, the sneaky way that Irish priest looked at me and cracked jokes and played with those bones, he's trying to make me, and do you know something, girl, you're going to let yourself get made, why not—?

Again the Count clears his throat . . .

"My ancestors were Swedes . . . they came to Italy during that last disastrous Crusade . . . You've heard of the Crusades, I suppose—?"

"Now look—! I'm not all *that* ignorant. I mean, even if I *do* earn my living as a dancer, after all we Americans do know a little bit about *European* history . . . Doc Kunster: A survey of European History 101—"

"I beg your pardon—"

"No. I was just thinking of my sophomore Humanities professor in college. A refugee from Germany. Everybody said he was queer, but once during comprehensive exams he tried to slip his hand up my dress—"

The Count's laugh is a brittle shadow, his eyes cloud wistfully, his eyelids lower like furtive window shades, his nostrils twitch: "And what did you do, I mean it must have been somewhat embarrassing for you—"

"What did I do? I told him to take his slimy hand out from under my dress, that's what I did, said—"

"And—the er-uh, professor?"

"He started crying, he got on his knees, he begged me not to report him to the president, he said he couldn't help what he did on account of I reminded him of Aïda —she's an Ethiopian queen—I got an A out of the course without even having to finish the exam—"

Raffaele finishes the wine in his glass. He is blushing. He swallows and nervously clears his throat and says: "You know, I had no idea you had a university degree. Here in Italy we—"

"I don't. I ran out of money after my sophomore year and had to go to work as a waitress—"

"Oh, what a pity—"

"Oh, I wouldn't say so. It's the first smart thing I did

in my life. I might have ended up a social worker—that's what I was studying to be, a social worker—"

A buglike 500 Fiat pulls up into the driveway. Eagerly the waiter rushes to the door. He flicks his napkin against his grease-stained black trousers, pantingly, like a house-bred hound wagging its tail. The Count reaches across the table and takes Doris' hand. It is surprisingly limp and birdlike, very warm, and a tiny nerve is throbbing in the small of the wrist. As Doris turns to look toward the door (the waiter is leading two mud-caked hunters across the room: the taller hunter slips his gun off his shoulders and says as he slumps down wearily on the chair the waiter is holding for him: *"Accidenti che pioggia—!"*), the Count, who is slyly observing Doris, is suddenly reminded of gold and rubies, of black Byzantine madonnas, amulets and incensed prayers. Annoyed at the way the two hunters are boldly ogling her (for through her long warm fingers he can feel her whole body expand like a watch spring suddenly released: aware of the mud-caked hunters' virile devotion, Doris throws her head back and laughs, pulls away her hand, fumbles nervously in her brocade handbag for her lipstick and begins to stripe her pouting lips a waxy ruby red), the Count says, surprised at the uncontrolled tremor of jealousy in his voice: "I'm sure you would have made a perfectly marvelous social worker—I can just see you, visiting lonely old men in their shabby rented rooms, massaging their trodden egos and lecturing them on the need for moral uplift . . ."

"I suppose your idea of social workers is a kind of poor man's call girl—"

"Well, to tell you the truth, I have little sympathy for what you Americans call 'social workers'—especially women. Somehow they all seem part of some international feminine conspiracy to make us men suffer for the drudgery their mothers had to endure in a young country without servants or slaves, and before the washing machine was invented—"

"Hold on a minute, Count—I'll have you know my mother worked all her life as a maid, and her mother's mother was a slave—so just what in the hell are you talking about, anyway?"

"I'm sorry—"

Raffaele is blushing (he hears one of the hunters say in coarse Roman dialect what sounds like "*A—mazzache-pezzodifica, e purecioccolatoè!*"), he stiffens and calls the waiter imperiously: "*Cameriere!*"

The waiter comes rushing to the table, but backtracks to drop a plastic-covered menu on the mud-caked hunters' table: "*Comandi?*"

"*Il conto, per favore—*"

Raffaele looks down at his gold Omega watch. It is nearly five fifteen. He wonders whether he should call the office, but decides against it: Higgins can take care of anything important that comes up. Having made this decision, he relaxes and smiles and suavely says to Doris: "I think you'll like my apartment—"

"Who says I'm going to your apartment?"

(*2 1*)

"I insist—"

"Well, Count—if you insist—"

Doris laughs again and begins smoothing her skirt. She looks over at the mud-caked hunters; she exchanges inflammatory glances with them. The mud-caked hunters look away like embarrassed schoolboys, the taller hunter stomps his boot on the floor, he calls boisterously for the waiter: *"Ocaminiere, quisimuoredifame!"*

It is three o'clock in the morning. Doris and the Count are asleep in the Count's huge baroque-sculptured bed. Doris is naked. One arm rests limply along the bas-relief contours of her body swathed in crumpled sheets. The Count wears pale yellow silk pajamas and there is a determined smile on his lips as though sleep for him is a far more serious business than wakefulness. He sleeps in an adult version of the prenatal position; his fists, joined together beneath his chin, are tightly clenched. A wide valley of cotton and cashmere separates them. There is no harmony to their breathing, though neither snores. The only light in the bedroom, more a phosphorescent glow, comes from the circular dial of a radio which has been left turned on. The radio hums like a miniature factory. There is a crucifix over the bed. There are two gilded baroque angels at the foot of the bed. There are no photographs in the room, but a water-color portrait of a circle hangs on the wall; Doris' clothes are spread out carelessly on a silk-covered divan. A white garter belt and a pair of silk stockings lie on the floor next to the bed like relics washed ashore by the tide. Down on the street, four floors below, the night watchman passes: the tires of his bicycle swish smoothly on the sidewalk, he whistles jauntily in time with the jingling of his keys. There is a half-empty bottle of whiskey on the low table in front of the silk-covered divan. One of the two glasses is still almost full. There is an overturned ashtray on the handwoven rug beneath the table. Most of the butts are long and lipstick-rimmed and there are many olive pits mixed with the scattered mound of ashes. Near the overturned ashtray there is a damp liquid stain: does it looks like blood? . . .

Suddenly the radio coughs and splutters and Doris stirs in her sleep. She is dreaming. "What are you doing down here at this time of night?" the Irish priest asks. "Don't you know visitors aren't allowed down here in the Catacombs at this time of night?" Doris jerks herself awake. She sits up with a start and looks around the room. Moonlight or the bright glow of a street light filters in an almost perfect rectangular design through the closed shutters. There is a bad fuzzy taste in her mouth and only now does it occur to her that there must have been garlic in the salad. She looks around on the bed table at her side for a cigarette, but the package of Lucky Strikes is empty. Running her tongue over her teeth, forcing a surge of saliva to rise in her mouth to rinse away the bad fuzzy taste, she reaches over and wakes up the Count . . .

"Raffaele . . . Raffaele . . . wake up, what time is it, anyway?"

The Count wakes up, he turns on the bed lamp, in a

(23)

matter of moments he is well-groomed and smiling—almost as if, in the instant between wakefulness and sleep, he had somehow rushed to the bathroom, urinated, washed, shaved and combed his hair.

"*Buon giorno,*" he says, turning over on his side to face Doris, who instinctively pulls the sheets over her small firm breasts, which in the rose glow of the bed lamp have the silken purplish sheen of eggplants.

"What time is it? You don't happen to have a cigarette, do you?"

Raffaele picks up his watch, he holds the dial close to his eye, he shakes it, and says: "It's three o'clock in the morning, and if you open that drawer there, there ought to be some cigarettes in there . . ."

In the drawer there are no cigarettes but there is a long fat cigar wrapped in crackling cellophane. The Count strikes a match and lights the cigar for Doris. She blows out a cloud of fragrant tobacco smoke. The blue smoke clings to her naked shoulders and breasts like morning clouds clinging to valleys and hills. Through the smoke her eyes gleam like moonlight reflected in a well. The Count runs a finger along the slightly sunken curve where the aggressive tilt of her breasts begins. The purple nipples stiffen, they become vibrantly alive. Impulsively Raffaele throws his arms around her waist and buries his head in her lap. He rotates his head in the warm depression, in the fleshy trinity of pelvis and thighs—I am a rhinoceros wallowing in the muddy delta of the Nile . . .

"What I mean," Doris says, as, studiously, in perfect

four-four time, she runs her fingers through his brittle close-cropped blond hair, "what I mean is, if you've only been to bed with *one* white woman before—I mean how can you generalize about what white women are like—?"

"Doris . . . Doris . . . *non sono stato mai così felice in tutta la mia vita!*"

"Do you mind handing me that ashtray over there?"

"I'll never go to bed with another white woman as long as I live!"

Without changing position he reaches for the ashtray and places it on the pillow with a muscle-straining back-hand gesture. Doris staidly flicks the flaky white ashes into the amber-colored ashtray. She blows out another cloud of fragrant tobacco smoke and her expression becomes thoughtful as she says: "You're the first white man I've ever been to bed with . . ."

"I don't believe you . . ."

"No kidding, the very first . . ."

"And . . . men of your own . . . race . . . ?"

"Only one . . . and it wasn't in bed . . . it was in the back of a station wagon along the Pennsylvania Turnpike . . ."

"But—"

"You think girls in show business have a lot of affairs; you think just because a girl's a dancer—"

"Doris, *bellezza mia* . . . then you're practically a virgin . . ."

"Not after tonight I'm not—"

Again Doris and the Count make love. Time expands and contracts, consciousness drifts violently from brain to hands and fingers, to unexplored patches of flesh, nerve ends burn with a cold fierce light. Gradually breathing assumes the rectangular minuette cadence of rational thought and life. Tiny beads of perspiration dot the Count's hairline, like a microscopic crown of pearls. He picks up Doris' dead cigar from the floor and lights it. The flame flickers, his hands are shaking. Doris gets up and goes to the window. She pulls open the shutters. The sky has brightened with the approaching dawn. Birds twitter in the majestic pine tree across the street. (Which bird has first heard the rising of the sun?) Graceful and confident is her pose as she stands silhouetted against the glass. At this haunted hour between night and day it is as if Doris has never known the atrocious innocence of clothes . . .

. . . "But how do you know you're pregnant?" I ask (today is a gray day, the clouds are sullen and refuse to rise, the air stands still, numb and defiant, like weary workers after ninety days on strike; last night in the pizzeria my—for me—interesting conversation with B. about American show business, especially the showboats that used to ply the Ohio and Mississippi rivers; we compared the time—time, always time—it takes for the act of fingers touching the keys of a harpsichord, which is plucked, and a calypso on a showboat, which involves the passage of steam through long narrow pipes, souls through labyrinths, air through the organ pipes of Bach, father and son; but this conversation, extremely interesting to me, kept being interrupted by a Spanish poet in exile who wanted to talk about bullfights and Moors, he said that eroticism and mysticism are the same soup, he said, he said—and the morning's papers full of revolts, Argentina, Syria, Algeria, *uffa;* Doris is wearing a sober gray flannel suit; today is March 31) . . .

"I'm pregnant, all right . . . I've been vomiting up everything I've eaten for the last two days!"

"But are you sure?" (What *really* are my feelings? Does Doris know that the Count has a wife?)

III

Three young athletic priests walk through the door. Who are they? Why do they wear black (cassocks, kilts, skirts)? Now come two more young priests. But these beardless young priests wear glasses. Should a writer have a beard? Is a writer father or is a writer son? Reynolds Packard has a beard (Rome correspondent for the *Daily News*, dean of the foreign press corps, already a war correspondent when Mussolini invaded Ethiopia;

Doris, Aïda, Ethiopian queen). His tall broad-boned wife has just walked out the door (I am writing in a German beer garden on Via della Croce). In the public relations office of the British airline on Via Veneto, Higgins is asking the Count, as he reads about Elizabeth Taylor's rumored divorce in *Il Messaggero* and suspiciously steals a glance at the thorn-stemmed red rose in a brand new crystal vase on the Count's desk: "By the way, when is Easter this year . . . ?" On the Cleopatra set in Cinecittà, near the Catacombs on the Appian Way, Doris gazes pensively into a cup of coffee and tries to read the future, then gives up . . .

Over my head is an image, Rembrandt-like, darkly varnished, painted on wood (*Ein Tip bei dem ich nie verbier* BIER: who of you remembers when, in America, there was a craze for making pictures, *burning* pictures of reindeer and snow-capped mountains—time, always time, listening, always listening, billions of years of imprisoned memory undistilled, electric-pointed stylus, plastic ballpoint pen) of St. Hubert Priez Pour Nous! At St. Hubert's side there are two dogs—one black, the other white; St. Hubert gazes toward the Light; the Light is a circle; in the circle of light there is a proud majestic reindeer. T. says, and Emma agrees, that you cannot kill a reindeer if he looks you in the eye. *St. Hubert Priez Pour Nous!* Where is the Grail, the Holy Grail? Pawned in Paris, Monte di Pietà? The Algerian War is finally over, but yesterday the Secret Army terrorists murdered forty Moslems, patients in a hospital in

Oran, machine gun and plastic bomb. Tyrolean Adam and Eve: sunflower and marguerite. At the writers' congress in Florence where I first met T., the deaf English poet, David Wright asked plaintively: "Why are we here?" (the bleating of sheep) . . .

Today is yesterday and T., Alice and I are seated at Rosati's café in Piazza del Popolo waiting for P., the movie director. Alice hopes to get a small part in P.'s new film, *La Mamma*. While we are waiting for P. to come I let Alice read the first chapter of this novel. When she finishes, she asks me how the novel is going to end, what is going to happen to Doris. This is what I tell her . . .

"Well, first, I should tell you how I happened to meet Doris in the first place. Doris is the daughter of a girl I was in love with my freshman year in college. This was back in 1941. Barbara Clavers was my first big love affair. We'd go to the library every evening after dinner to study or listen to classical records. Then, on our way back to her dorm, we'd stop to sit down on a bench near the railroad tracks and watch the Pullmans and dining cars of the fast express go by. That's one of the reasons why we decided we'd get married and come to Europe to live, seeing all those rich people flash by in the dining cars with waiters holding up wine bottles for their approval. Once Barbara and I went to one of the most expensive Negro restaurants in town, one Sunday afternoon, to spend the ten dollars I won in an essay contest sponsored by the local NAACP chapter, and when I ordered a bottle of French wine the waitress burst out laughing and asked me what did I think this joint was, a— Well, what do you want with your meal, coffee or milk? Whiskey and a Tom Collins setup will cost you three dollars fifty, on account of today's Sunday . . .

"That's the first time I ever saw Bulldozer. He came into the restaurant while we were ordering with two members of his gang. Bulldozer's official activity was as undertaker. But being an undertaker was just a front for his being a numbers racketeer. Bulldozer was a gangster, big and black, with white hair and gold teeth, and there wasn't anything or anybody he was afraid to laugh at. His favorite sport was to ride around the campus and see pretty college girls with college boy friends. He'd ride around the campus in the afternoon in that big black Cadillac of his that looked just like a hearse and he'd cruise about like a deep sea fisherman fishing for a pretty girl to steal away from her college boy friend. When he found a pretty college girl he liked, the next day or so one of his henchmen would get in touch with the girl and slip her a brand new fifty-dollar bill and tell her that Bulldozer would be waiting for her that night in the parking lot next to his funeral parlor . . . I almost went crazy when I found out that Bulldozer had made Barbara pregnant and that she was going to be expelled. But just about that time I was drafted into the Army and I forgot all about Barbara until one day a month or so ago Doris called me up and told me that she was the daughter of an old college friend of mine, Barbara Clavers, and that she was in Rome, working as a dancer in the Cleopatra film, and that her mother had told her to look me up and that she'd found my address and telephone number at the American embassy, and would I mind if she came by, because there was something she wanted to ask my advice about . . ."

(Today is April 10. I read in this morning's edition of the *Rome Daily American* about the Secret Army: "Police said charges of six pounds of plastic each were set off almost simultaneously in the chemistry and biology laboratories in the Institute for the Study of Solar Energy and in front of the office of the dean of the Law School." Just before the first bird heard the rising of the morning sun, I had a strong dream tattooed on my consciousness: I dreamed of Prince Vittorio Massino; there was a party; I met a golden black-eyed Saracen pirate girl; in her presence there was joy and musical sorrow, not suffering; she said to Prince Vittorio, 'Come on, Prince, let's go and have a dance!' Then a social worker called. The question is whether Alice should enter a clinic or not. The social worker was warm and kind, her voice was like the voice of the golden black-eyed Saracen pirate girl; hearing her voice there was joy and musical sorrow, not suffering. I have only met Alice twice, I cannot give you the information you seek. And Signor T.? I met him at the Writers' Congress. I know nothing about him either. The doctor says that my son —you did not know that I am married?—the doctor says that my son possibly has German measles. The doctor asks my wife: "Has the boy taken any medicines?" Higgins is worried about the Count. The Count has come to the office unshaven. Higgins thinks the Count looks somewhat haggard; he clears his throat and starts to say—

Today is April 12: I have wasted a whole day translating a film script, *The Great Gladiator* . . . I feel tired and bored like an IBM computer turned to rubber. This is the last scene of *The Great Gladiator:*

GLADIATORS' QUARTERS BENEATH
GRANDSTAND. INT. DAY
As Brenno closes the door behind him, the cheering dies down and fades into the *LOVE THEME MUSIC.*

Brenno leans wearily against the door, hardly able to stand up.

Suddenly now a door opens and he sees Fabiola standing before him.

For a long time they stand there gazing at each other, silently, as though neither were willing to break the dreamlike enchantment.

Then Fabiola runs up to him and throws her arms

around him. Brenno draws her close in a strong embrace, an embrace as strong and binding as the love
that unites them. DISSOLVE TO
THE END

And now the phone rings. It is T. He has called to say
that Alice's grandfather died last night, that she has entered the clinic for a much-needed rest, and that perhaps
we shall meet tomorrow night at Rosati's. Last night
the Secret Army terrorists bombed the Italian TV station only three blocks from where I live. I am helping to
prepare a TV program here in Rome about Harlem that
will feature Louis Armstrong. I am tired writing so I
open the evening edition of *Telesera* and read: "Florence, April 12. A 27-year-old tailor, Mario Zuccalà,
claims to have spoken with two men from Mars who
told him that on April 20 they will deliver a message for
humanity. Here is the incredible story as told by the
young man. On his way home from Florence where he
works, yesterday evening about 9:15, Zuccalà, in the
vicinity of the town of Cidinella, suddenly felt a strong,
violent current. Turning, he saw a space ship, a 'flying
saucer.' Two men from Mars captured him and told
him: 'When the moon is in its fourth quarter, at one
A.M., we shall return to give you a message to consign to
humanity' . . ." April 20 is Good Friday. April 21 is the
Saint Day of Saint Anselm, 1033-1109, Archbishop of
Canterbury, theologian and philosopher, the propounder
of the ontological argument for the existence of God,

born at Aosta in Piedmont, of noble family, in his greatest work, *Cur Deus Homo,* 1094-98, he undertakes to make plain, even to infidels, the rational necessity of the Atonement . . . *id quo maius cogitari non potest* . . . Today is Friday, April 13. The Shah of Persia, Zoroastra, is visiting Washington, D.C. This morning's edition of *Il Paese* reports: "Paris, April 13. There are rumors circulating that Jacques Soustelle, ex-Gaullist leader, has been killed in South America by anti-Secret Army Agents." Today is Monday, April 16. Last Saturday, Bill P. phoned and said he would pass by in fifteen minutes to take me to Palazzo Brancaccio where the Incontro Internazionale for the Liberty of the Spanish People was taking place. Police swarmed about in the square, outside the palazzo. Fascist toughs lurked around the entrance like catfish waiting to be sucked into a sewer. Inside, there was an air of almost unbearable tension. The night before, Fascist terrorists broke into the palazzo and stole the hand-painted banner which had been sent clandestinely to the Congress by a group of political prisoners in Spain. Nenni, Pajetta, Rossi—that *other* generation, that *other* hour when the slimy dinosaur raised its head out of the stagnant stinking pond. I talked with Kingsley Martin about the theory of this novel. He listened and watched me. Bill P. took our photographs. At twelve-thirty I was to step up on the platform and read a statement on behalf of the American writers, up to now unrepresented at the Congress. A wild wind tormented the palm trees in the courtyard. Police inspectors were working with tape measures at the window, trying to discover how the Fascist terrorists managed to break in the night before. I stand before the microphone and hear my voice reading the statement in my hand. I listen with surprise. My voice is calm. My hands do not tremble. I know that I am frightened and yet I do not feel fright. The phone rings. It is Alice calling from the clinic. They have not put her to sleep, tranquillizers and a liquid that tastes like horse piss, she says. She wants to know why T. hasn't called. I don't know, but when he calls at one o'clock I'll tell him she called. Palm Sunday, yesterday, was gray and gloomy, but this morning the sun shines gloriously. We are still seated at Rosati's, waiting for P., the movie director. I am telling Alice how the novel shall end. I go on to say: "Now where was I? Oh, yes. Well, what Doris wanted to ask my advice about was whether I knew the Count and did I think he was reliable. Doris falls in love with the Count. She gets pregnant. The Count can't marry her. He wants her to have an abortion. The Count installs her in a fancy apartment in Parioli. The Cleopatra troupe leaves for Egypt. Doris is out of work. She refuses to have the abortion at the last minute. In the eighth month, she becomes dangerously depressed. In the meantime I have fallen in love with Doris. I am unable to distinguish in my mind and memory which is Doris and which is Barbara. I was the one who insisted that Doris did not have the abortion. There must be some continuity in flesh and blood as well as in dream and memory. I become depressed. I phone

Doris' mother. I phone Barbara. Barbara arrives by jet. She is here. Which is Doris? Which is Barbara? Barbara wants to visit the Catacombs. All three of us should go. At the last moment, I have a phone call. Important work in the movies. Doris and her mother go together to visit the Catacombs. Doris falls down the steep narrow steps. Her child is born prematurely in the Catacombs. The Irish priest does not know what to do. He holds a hand-kerchief helplessly over Doris' head. An Austrian tourist, a woman, a painter, pushes through the crowd and assists Doris. The life cry of the child shatters the underground silence of the martyrs' tombs. That is how the novel ends . . ."

And now, as the lights come on in Piazza del Popolo, like pearls materializing in the undersea twilight, the obelisk in the center of the square sways, and Alice says: "Well, I don't know . . . I mean, I don't think that's the way women have children . . . what I mean is, I'm not sure that's the way the novel should end . . ."

(Today is Tuesday, April 17. At the RAI-TV studios, three blocks from my home, we filmed the opening sequence to the show with Louis Armstrong. Before I left home, I telephoned Alice. She was well, she said. She sounded well and rested. She asked me if I had any news of P. Louis Armstrong shook my hand and said that I was a good actor, that I should make acting my career. Truman Young, the trombone player, said that I was going to make a lot of money as a writer. Photographers took pictures of Louis Armstrong and me shaking hands. I read in the evening papers that a shepherd was killed and run over three times on the twenty-third kilometer of the Via Pontina, which is not far from our vineyard. Today is Thursday, April 19. The responsible press is indignant because the Fascist agitators who attacked members of the Congress for the Libertà per il Popolo Spagnolo while they were leaving Palazzo Brancaccio at the end of the session the day I read a statement on behalf of the American writers, received only light fines. In this morning's edition of *Il Giorno* I read that P., who has been accused of trying to hold up a gas station in Latina, has offered to take "truth serum" and undergo questioning by all those journalists of the extreme right who have been so mercilessly, and unjustly, attacking him. In this morning's *Il Messaggero* I read that an "iguana," a miniature dinosaur, was found walking around in Piazza San Silvestro. Says the news story: "But in spite of its repelling aspect, the iguana is a docile and unoffensive reptile, easily domesticated. What is surprising is that a signora enjoys keeping around her such a monstrous animal . . ." The "signora" is a South American woman wearing an expensive fur who was riding around in an automobile with diplomatic license plates. All week the newspapers have been full of animals, flowers, poisons, strange and violent deaths. Truly we are in a Gothic age: the Year of the Plague is here. In the same edition of *Il Messaggero*, Orsola Nemi has a short story entitled "The Shadow of the Earth." "*If the*

Devil exists, then God exists . . ." What is she trying to say? What are they trying to say? Doesn't *she . . .* don't *they . . . know?* My son is up from his sickbed, he is singing. I think he is inventing an Easter surprise . . . In the afternoon edition of *Paese Sera* there is an unusually long article about illegitimate saints in Paradise, with much space given to Saint George, patron saint of England, Saint George and the dragon! *Uffa!* Are we selling soap or are we trying to cast light on the reality of human existence?)

At last P. has come. Nervously, catlike, he steps out of his automobile. He does not see us. I call his name. He comes to the table and sits down. Alice is suddenly nervous. She begins to preen and assume a Hollywood mask of neorealistic charm. P. and I exchange glances. He is very pale and the shadow of a death's-head gleams through his thin hairless skin. I make the introductions. P. says nervously that he only has a few moments because his leading lady is waiting for him. To neutralize the crisscrossing of psychic tension which is already creating a whirlwind void over the table, I tell P. that I am writing a novel and that we are discussing how it should end, and that this conversation about how the novel shall end is the central theme of the third chapter. At once P. is interested: I think he already has heard of the novel, because at the Writers' Congress in Florence I talked about it freely with anyone who was willing to listen. One novelist even began to criticize the novel as though it had already been written, which is perfectly in harmony with the theory of cubistic time I am so reck-lessly fooling around with. At the same time P. steals shrewd glances at Alice. He tells her that the main parts have already been filled but that in fifteen days (Today is the fifteenth day. Today is Good Friday. Eddie Fisher, Cleopatra's husband, will divorce Elizabeth Tay-lor to marry Natalie Wood, wife of Robert Wagner, who did not get the Oscar because it had to be given to Sophia Loren. My wife thinks that she is pregnant. If she is, which I doubt, the child would be born some time around Christmas. My wife, my son and my mother-in-law have gone to the Vatican to buy Easter eggs, whis-key and cigarettes in the company of a mysterious maker of watches—time, always time, listening, always listen-ing. On the cover of *Time* magazine there is a portrait of the German theologian Karl Barth: "The goal of human life is not death, but resurrection." The author of the cover story studied at St. Anselm's Priory School in Washington, D.C. *Il Giorno* says in a big front-page headline: PASQUA CALDA E BELLA) he will have a small part for her . . .

When P. leaves, T., Alice and I go to a nearby piz-zeria. We eat, drink, we talk wildly until all the other customers have left. We lurch through the streets of Rome, carried along by strange surging spiritual tides, like homing pigeons, like salmon . . . until we end up at a terrifyingly lurid bar, filled with gold-covered chocolate Easter eggs that line the wall and hang suspended from the ceiling, like bombs about to fall, or drops of dew; inside that bar there is a suffocating junglelike atmosphere of pregnancy, the glaring white neon, the gold foil, eggs, dewdrops, bombs—whatever they are, they are ready to fall. I *know:* Something is going to happen, somewhere a dewdrop shall fall, eggs shall fall, bombs shall fall . . .

Alice giggles. T. sustains her (all three of us are drunk). A sly broken-toothed photographer takes our picture as the three of us embrace.

(The Count is phoning Doris. There is no answer. He frowns. Higgins looks up from his copy of *Il Giorno*— because of the Fiera di Milano he is reading Milan newspapers this week—and, observing the Count's nervousness, he says: "I read in *Il Giorno* that Easter's going to be hot this year . . .")

My wife and son have just come back from the Vatican with a gold-covered Easter egg: on the gold-covered Easter egg are two artificial roses. I ask my son: "Who chose this particular egg?" My son replies: "*La mamma* . . ." On Easter Day we shall open the egg: What will be the surprise inside? The twelve o'clock siren sounds . . .

Something is going to happen . . .

It is seven o'clock in the evening. A. and his wife are sitting at Rosati's café. The lights come on (like pearls materializing in the undersea dusk, and the obelisk in the center of the square sways) and newsboys (actually they are shrewd frog-voiced men) shout the incredible

Good Friday news: General Salan, head of the Secret Army, has been arrested! News of his arrest reached the wire services at 2:15. Elated, terrified with joy, I think: Salan must have been arrested when the twelve o'clock siren sounded . . .

"Did you have a nice Easter?" Higgins asks the Count. Today is Tuesday, April 24, and the Count is reading the headlines of the morning edition of *Il Messaggero:* De Gaulle decided to normalize the situation in Algeria . . . France is getting ready to begin a vast offensive against the OAS . . . The French president has delivered to General Fourchet, commander-in-chief of the troops in Algeria, personal and written instructions to proceed immediately and with all means to the complete control of Algeria and Oran where the OAS is applying the total blockade of the Moslem quarters . . . Uneasiness in government circles for the social agitation . . . After the strike of the railway workers also the postal workers have threatened to strike . . .

The Count carefully folds the newspaper and places it beside the white alabaster vase on his desk. The rose has begun to wither. The Count lights his pipe and leans back in his imitation leather relax-chair.

"Oh, nothing special," he says through a cloud of fragrant tobacco smoke, "didn't leave the city, all that traffic, thought I'd stay in Rome for a change, see the city from a tourist's point of view . . ."

(Today is yesterday, Easter Monday, *Pasquetta.* Doris

and the Count are strolling through Villa Borghese. On Easter Sunday it rained. Now the sun burns fiercely. The shadows on the marble statues are sharp and tinged green and violet. Birds are plump and arrogant as they strut over the grass, pregnant with spring. Yesterday was the birthday of Rome . . .)

IV

Today is May 2. The sun is bright and diamond-cut, not a cloud in the sky, the earth breathes calm and freely, tomorrow there will be few crimes reported in the morning papers. Yesterday was The Day of the Workers, May Day. The sky sullen, a low-browed resentful sky, the air electric with the secretly dueling cross currents of "ancient struggles of class." Millions of words pronounced over countless microphones: full bellies preaching to shrewd suspicious eyes. Workers, Masters, both secretly asking themselves: Who is Master, who is Slave, who will pay my bills when His Excellency the IBM machine lubricates his smooth-humming smile and asks Master Worker would he mind stepping aside? . . .

And Doris? So much has happened and I have been so busy that I have had little time to think of her. On Easter morning she called to say that she wasn't pregnant after all and that she was going away with the Count for a short vacation on Capri. She sounded happy, a bit giddy, I thought. On Easter morning my wife also told me that she wasn't pregnant after all. On Easter morning I read in the morning papers that General Salan had been arrested at exactly 12:05. On Easter Day, said the next day's papers, more animals were born at the Rome Zoo than on any day in the last fifty years. The Cleopatra super-colossal is again in crisis because of Elizabeth Taylor's divorce from Eddie Fisher and open courtship of Richard Burton, who plays the part of Marc Antony in the film. Public relations, truth or fiction? I am beginning to have the strangest feeling that we are all nothing more than shadows, spirits, breathed into life and manipulated by Pirandello's fertile mind.

Today is May 3. Again the sun is bright and diamond-cut, again there is not a cloud in the sky, again the earth breathes calmly and freely, there are no crimes reported in the morning papers, but I am in a strange and agitated mood. Yesterday afternoon Doris called and on sudden impulse I invited her home for dinner. For some reason which I do not yet understand, I had put off introducing Doris to my wife, though on more than one occasion Doris had hinted broadly that she would like very much to see my son. In ten years of marriage, I have had only three or four extramarital relationships, all of them furtive and short-lived. Perhaps the fact that I am writing a novel about Doris, that I have secretly taken possession of her soul, if not her body, other than in fantasy (alas, my trade is that of a writer), explains the all too obvious state of nervousness I was in when, promptly at eight-thirty, she arrived.

She was stunningly dressed, and wore no make-up except the black-edged Cleopatra hieroglyphics around her eyes. Her dress was of soft wool, very loose, and somehow revealed her taut curves more than if the dress had been tight. The dress was the melancholy red of sunset (West: Mae West), which enriched the chestnut brown of her complexion, and her long rounded nails were painted in exactly the same hue. Her perfume, in the hallway as she passed the kitchen, mixed with the aroma of roasting meat and became an alien presence in the house, as when a priest and *chierichetto* enter for the traditional Easter blessing . . .

My son showed Doris his stamp collection, and Doris went with him to watch the evening TV publicity shorts and the only TV program he really enjoys. Then to the ill-concealed annoyance of Angela, my son's nurse, Doris insisted on undressing him and putting him to bed. While this was going on, my wife, taking advantage of the fact that we were momentarily alone, looked at me innocently and said:"*Carina, la tua bella . . .*" When she said that, some gnawing sense of shame or resentment (perhaps I was jealous that my fictional Doris was being contaminated by the prosaic intimacy of my domestic life, or perhaps I was afraid that my wife, as on so many occasions before, was reading the stormy weather map of my mind) prodded me into saying with savage rudeness: "*Idiota!*" Even before the word crossed my lips, I was sorry and contrite, but for the rest of the evening my wife was coldly polite but distant, and the meal was one of those dreamlike playlets in which the characters speak too fast and are always saying excuse me for overrunning the other's phrase.

As always in such awkward situations, dripping with guilt, and feeling responsible for the disaster of the meal, I drank too much and made a pitiful effort to be witty. At a certain point in the evening, I painted a mustache on my face and made an embarrassingly heavy-handed imitation of a Sicilian baron courting a Swedish actress. By this time, my wife and Doris had become female allies and were exchanging commiserating glances. Finally, to make things worse, I clumsily tried to kiss Doris while we were waiting for a taxi at the taxi stand in Piazza Mazzini. When I finished kissing her soft but tightly pursed lips (the inward trumpeting of giant bees inhaling intoxicating pollen), she furtively touched the back of her hand aganst her mouth and said dreamily: "Your wife is so nice, I like Italian women, there's something about their eyes, they weep without tears, as if they have seen and known everything there is to see and to know . . ."

To cover up my embarrassment (how many times has the word "embarrassment" appeared already in this novel?) I asked Doris when I would be seeing her again: "We've got to get on with our novel, you know . . ." Doris eased her slim body into the taxi like a lovely corpse easing itself into a casket, and through the rear mirror the fat heavy-browed taxi driver ogled Doris' legs as her skirt slipped far above her knees, and suddenly a shuddering cold wave of jealousy swept over me; suddenly I was ferociously jealous of the Count, I was jealous of the stratified secrecy of Rome, jealous of Italian men, with their clinical vulgar eye-fondling, their cynically nonchalant flowery courtesan talk, their cynical mother-instigated sadism toward women born outside the mother-dominated home . . .

Doris smiled at the taxi driver and, in sugarly prim and haltingly precise Italian, gave the address of her apartment. Then, as the driver explosively and unnecessarily gunned the motor, she shouted over the smoky roar: "Maybe tomorrow, darling—but, honey, whatever you do, now don't neglect your homework with that charming wife of yours . . . ! "

Today is May 6. Alice just called to say that she had a letter from T. He is in Milan. The night before he left we went together to the Circolo degl' Artisti. Celebrating his departure, we drank too much. In the company of an Ethiopian ras and a young Iraqi student we found ourselves at dawn in the all-night café of the railroad station. I told the young Ethiopian that I was a king. He told me that, though he worked as a waiter at the Circolo degl' Artisti, he was a ras. T. told me that he was my brother. The young Iraqi told me that I was the reincarnation of Mohammed. While all this was going on there was a knock-down-and-drag-out fight in Alice's apartment. She ended up in the police station. The police interrogated her and tried to make her confess that she was a prostitute. They did not know that she is an actress (spirits, shadows, breathed into life, manipulated by Pirandello's fertile mind). T., the Ethiopian ras and the Iraqi student vanished down the street. The morning light was quicksilver and harsh, the light of day was terrifyingly real. Midst the nervous traffic of Romans going to work, I felt unpeeled, no longer a king, exposed, a timid youth stealing out of a whore house. It was seven o'clock in the morning when I got home. I had to awaken my wife and borrow a thousand lire from my mother-in-law to pay the slyly smiling taxi driver . . .

Today is May 12. Doris and the Count are here to watch the TV program *Il Signore delle 21: Harlem*, in which I appear as a kind of assistant master of ceremonies, together with Louis Armstrong, Sammy Davis, Hazel Scott, the Peters Sisters and many other stars of the Negro entertainment world. I know that this is the first time that so many Negro entertainers have appeared at one time on a European television program and I am frankly apprehensive. Strange things happened during the Ampex recording of the program. For years I had lived under the illusion that racial prejudice does not exist in Italy, which has now become my second *patria*. And yet —had I been imagining things?

(Today is May 23. My son has been ill and his illness has numbed the time muscle of my mind. Segni has been elected president of the Republic. Accattone has been sentenced to a year and three months for his drunken insults. Josephine Baker has appeared on another *Signore delle 21* program dedicated to *"soubrettes"* and has adopted another baby. The OAS tried to assassinate De Gaulle and failed. Alice has had several days' work in P.'s film but is disgusted with—time, always time, listening, always listening!)

Today is June 14. For nearly a month now I have been absent, hibernating, hiding away from the terrifying responsibility of this novel, like a criminal who has lost his nerve and become addicted to the secretive self-righteous vice of drinking milk and eating mashed sardines spread on Eucharistic soda crackers. The day after my son was pronounced well and cured I contracted the mumps. The TV program was a great success. Fifteen million Italians approved. I feel personally responsible for this success. The next morning I went to the barber for a haircut, the first time in more than six months. My last haircut was in Washington, D.C. My sister Dorothy wanted me to wear my hair long during my two-week stay in America. She said that with my hair long I looked "so European." My mother insisted that I get a haircut so that I would look "more American."

After two weeks in bed with the mumps, I feel rested. In bed I felt protected from all that was happening in the world. The Americans were going to explode an atomic bomb in the Van Allen magnetic belt that circles the earth. The explosion failed, and I turned over beneath the warm rumpled sheets and continued to read a novel about the advertising industry in New York. While I was in bed with the mumps, Salan escaped the death penalty, though he admitted being responsible for the OAS crimes in Algeria; Eichmann was hanged in Israel and his ashes were scattered over the sea; Young Fascists in Rome invaded the ghetto at Portico d'Ottavia to post Fascist political posters on the wall of the synagogue during the recent election campaign; Carpenter orbited three times around the earth; in Portugal and in Spain workers are on strike . . .

Then, on Thursday evening, Ben Johnson phones to tell me that last night Laura committed suicide . . .

My first reaction is a feeling of guilt. Why, why did Laura want to kill herself? The evening papers call her a "Creole Beauty." Suddenly now I remember that B.J., shortly after I told him about the novel I was writing, asked me if Laura was my inspiration for Doris. I told him that of course she wasn't, that Doris was an entirely "invented" character. But is there such a thing as an entirely "invented" character? And now I remember something else: When J.P., Laura's husband, came back to her after the long (marital crisis) separation, during which he won a literary prize in London for a recently published book of poetry, he came to see me. When I told him about the novel I was writing, he warned me about talking about it too much (tertiary orders: vows of silence) lest I never get around to finishing it. Here in Rome there were three "mixed" marriages, that is, marriages between (Man and Woman) Negro and White: mine; B.J. and his Italian wife, Liliana; and J.P., who is Anglo-Irish, and Laura, who was West Indian. I turn back in this MS and discover with a shock that my description of Doris is almost a perfect description of Laura (". . . Her Cleopatra eyes blaze furiously (Doris is one of Elizabeth Taylor's handmaidens in Twentieth Century-Fox's Cleopatra colossal now being filmed in Rome and, though on several occasions I have tried to persuade her not to, she insists on wearing the grotesquely exotic—but, I must admit, for her, strangely appropriate—make-up she wears before the cameras; her hairdo, too, is authentically ancient Egyptian, a back-leaning cone which somehow makes me think of a black lacquered cone of spider webs, a magical fertility symbol floating detachedly over the masklike beauty of her enchanted nut-brown monkey face . . ."). My wife and I went to the funeral (Alice was so upset by the news of Laura's suicide that she returned to her psychiatrist: she spent hours dressing for the funeral, after telling me over the phone that she was thinking of committing suicide herself, then arrived too late, after everyone had left the cemetery). Most of the people gathered in the Protestant cemetery near the Pyramid were friends of Laura's from FAO where she worked as a secretary. There were not many of the "chic" wealthy crowd she had been frequenting during J.P.'s absence . . . My wife said she saw the son of the richest man in the world.

The grave-diggers were elegantly dressed in black tams. Their grave-digging uniforms were like the uniforms of the Vatican Swiss Guards dyed black; they were very efficient in a Swiss Calvinistic way. A wind blew and caused the pines to sway and drowned out the droning sound of the Protestant minister's reading of the funeral service. I stood close to M. He seemed to me to be the most sincerely moved of all. Observing his long aristocratic fingers which were tightly compressed, I remembered that I still owe him thirty pounds. Silone's wife, who was very fond of Laura, was dressed as for an embassy garden party, and I was grateful for her presence, for there was a strange hypocritical romantic staginess to that cemetery where so many Anglo-Saxons had come to take their dying breathing exercises of archaeological poetical scentless Grecian-urn *lussuria*. The Book of Common Prayer . . . Solemnly, in turn, my wife and I pick up the gardener's trowel the grave-digger offers like a bored waiter offering a tray of tidbits at a cocktail party. Somewhat self-consciously we spill earth on the polished wood casket, which has just been lowered into the shallow rectangular Swiss-perfect grave. Ashes to ashes, dust to dust . . . the earth is so powdery, like "earth" on the moon, that it makes no sound when it strikes the casket. Good-bye, Laura! We leave. My wife's eyes are tearful. I am trying desperately to think of something to think. Most of the people are heading for the exit near the chapel. The ludicrous thought comes to me that perhaps this is only one of those typically Roman *ricevimenti* where weak martinis and syrupy negronis are doled out to a shuffling herd of guests as wages for having sat through a boring lecture on minor metaphysical poets. B.J., Liliana, my wife and I hasten to a nearby bar. There, as the evening traffic gouges out an earsplitting circle around us, we all drink too much and too fast. B.J. and Liliana begin to quarrel about whether B.J. is neglecting Liliana too much: they are having "marital trouble" and, since I am drinking too much, I am having a "drinking problem"; my wife sides with Liliana and Liliana begins to cry. Liliana's tears come almost as a relief to my wife (or so I imagine), for I suspect that her profoundly pagan-Catholic sensitivity has somehow been offended by the tearless Swiss efficiency of Laura's passage to the Other World. It is time to go home. I hear Laura calling out: "James! James!" to my son as she sits laughing at our table, chattering gaily about sex and love. Oh, I did not like Laura. Strangely, I was never attracted to her physically, though last October, the night before I went to America, we did a grotesque dance together at a party she gave: we rolled around on the floor wildly like two bottles being spun in a children's kissing game . . . As soon as we get home I tell Emma, our cook, about the funeral, I describe it to her in detail. For Emma had been fond of Laura and had cut out the newspaper clippings about Laura's suicide to take home and place among her souvenirs. But when, winding up my description of the funeral, I mention how J.P., though his demeanor at the graveside was severely controlled, seemed to be suffering terribly, Emma suddenly becomes almost hysterical: "Oh, no! Not *them! They* never suffer! *They* never suffer remorse! We're the ones who have to pay! It's we women who suffer in the end!"

The Book of Common Prayer . . .

V

And here now this heat-crazed uncertain July. Gasping for breath, we crowd the stifling hot waiting room of the world and nervously watch the clock. Why doesn't it come, that for which we wait? Strikes, plane crashes, tornadoes—like a prematurely rotten fruit, this truant summer has an ugly malevolent edge. High over the Pacific, two hundred miles above the earth, the hydrogen bomb pricks a microscopic hole in the lightless Van

Allen radiation belt. Crowds stand on Waikiki Beach in Honolulu and marvel at the hell-fire reddish glow. Is Cancer Infectious? (*Life International*, July 16, 1962) Benny Goodman brings jazz to Russia. COMMIES CALL TEST BOMB WORK OF ATOMIC MANICS . . . The sound? What happened to the sound? Was it heard, the H-bomb's whisper, two hundred miles above the earth? It is July, and summer is here; let us leave the city, let us take refuge on the beach . . .

But first, another suicide: On Monday, July 2, General René de Larminat, president of the Military Court of Justice appointed by General De Gaulle to try General Salan for additional acts of sedition committed in prison after the scandalous trial before the Special Military Tribunal which resulted in his escaping the death penalty, pointed a pistol in his mouth and blew out his brains rather than face the possibility of having to sentence to death his highly decorated colleague in a new trial . . . The referendum in Algeria has resulted in an almost unanimous *"Oui!"* for independence, and the pirate OAS radio transmitter in Oran went on the air for the last time to proclaim dramatically: "Our struggle has become hopeless and therefore senseless. Algeria is dead, the will of God be done." The next day a crisis broke out in the FLN leadership, between Benkhedda, who heads the moderates, and the left-wing radicals under Vice-Premier Mohammed Ben Bella, who claims that the FLN is being too soft on the OAS terrorists and becoming too dependent on France . . . On the Fourth of

July—Independence Day in Rome went mainly uncelebrated among the American colony because economy measures prevented the ambassador from holding his traditional Fourth of July garden party at the ambassadorial residence—all Algeria was celebrating its independence; Benkhedda and the civilian chiefs of the FLN were cheered by crowds estimated at over a million, but Ben Bella, vice-president of the provisional government, had gone to Cairo, apparently to consult with Egyptian Premier Nasser . . . I have stopped my excessive drinking and, most important, stopped smoking—revenge on moralistic friends . . . mystery of vices . . . people beginning to feel guilty about using pills, drugs, antibiotics . . . In this morning's *La Stampa* I read: "FRANCE HAS TURNED OVER ALL POWERS TO INDEPENDENT ALGERIA— WISDOM AND MODERATION OF THE ARABS—In the euphoria of victory the Arabs have managed to maintain their nerves in place . . . So far there has been no sacking, nor vendettas, but only a massive requisitioning of private automobiles in which the Moslems ride through the streets exalting their newly acquired freedom . . . Benkhedda, chief of the provisional government, has received in Algeria the triumphant honors of an exulting crowd: the 'rebel' Ben Bella, perhaps on Nasser's advice, has renounced temporarily any plans he may have had for a coup . . ." On the front page of this morning's *Il Paese* I read: "SIXTH CASE OF FOCOMELIA . . . Another baby born dead and deformed in Torino . . . The mother, during the period of pregnancy, had taken sedatives . . . Torino, July 4—Another deformed baby born in Torino; and this is the sixth case in three months. The cause, at least according to preliminary investigation by sanitation authorities, is always the same: the use of pharmaceutical products, by the mother, during her pregnancy. Today's case of 'focomelia,' as it is called in medical terminology, is even more alarming than the preceding cases, because, as has been established by medical examination, the mother used only a sedative, the base of which was acido glutammico, and not, as in the other cases, 'thalidomide.' Thus it is supposed that there are numerous pharmaceutical specialties which might prove fatal to those who use them . . ." Immediately after reading this item, I open my desk drawer and pull out the package of pills Dr. C., who treated my case of mumps, recommended to me: on the back of the bright green box, I read: "Composition—each tablet contains 1-glutammina mg. 20, eccipient q.B. . . ." I must ask Dr. C. if there is any danger . . . My son is sick in bed again with a tenacious throat infection, but he eats like a horse and grows like a little giant! He also has become slightly patronizing toward me, and occasionally mocks my accent: sometimes I have the disconcerting feeling that time has turned back and that I am he, it is July 4, 1929, and I have just come back from Cadorri's drugstore with a pocket full of Chinese firecrackers . . .

But today is July 5, 1962, ten o'clock in the morning,

I am in Rome, Italy, and I am strangely disturbed by an article I have just read in *Vie Nuove*, a pro-leftist weekly, published in Rome. The article is by Lorenza Mazetti, a talented film director and novelist, a long-time friend.

The article appears in her weekly column, *"Chi Dice Donna,"* which title is borrowed from an old Italian proverb which goes, *"Chi dice donna, dice danno,"* or in English, "Who says woman, says damage," or in American slang, "Women mean trouble!" The article begins:

The Suicide of Laura

Laura, a friend of mine, has committed suicide. A beautiful girl who lived with an English poet. He earned not a lira. In compensation he was fascinating.

I believe all of snob Rome knew them. He very tall and imitated James Joyce as a young man, but without Joyce's genius, she dark with dreaming eyes.

They had all the ingredients of the modern couple, that is to say, the apparent attributes of the emancipated couple, the first of which is true love.

(The evening papers have just come out. I read in *Paese Sera:* "Bloody vendetta of the OAS in Algeria—100 dead and wounded in Oran—Oran, July 5—This morning, shortly after noon, the center of Oran unexpectedly has been the center of a violent and bloody gun fight. The management of the hospital communicated that within the space of 45 minutes over a hundred dead and wounded have been recovered. The crowd that jammed the center of Oran, when the shooting began, around 12:10 Rome time, tried to find cover in doorways or threw itself down on streets and sidewalks in prey of panic. For the moment there are no further details about the shooting nor is it known who started it. Units of the FLN took up positions in the downtown district soon after the shooting began. Around 12:25, in the center of Oran, there was still the sound of sporadic shooting . . .")

We all thought: they are happy, they love each other, they live together because they are in love.

And yet I feel that it was just their emancipation that killed them.

The freedom, the emancipation of the woman, the equal rights between man and woman, are all phases in a glass of water when the social-economic system is capitalist. These principles create victims.

The first victims of emancipation are the women. Laura's seems to me a typical case of the bourgeois ambiance, and only of the bourgeois ambiance.

She worked at the FAO (United Nations Food and Agricultural Organization) and as an independent woman she could permit herself the luxury of living with the man she loved. So she chose a young penniless poet.

The angry resentment of the male against the emancipation of the woman is an anger, a rancor that pervades all Americans and Englishmen and not yet the Italians, because the dominating class in Italy still dominates the woman who continues, in Italy, to be a slave, at least in the bourgeois classes. In the proletariat this *hate* does not exist because as Engels says in his book, *Origins of the Family, of Private Property and of the State*, in the proletariat class "true love" has always existed since marriage as a contract of interests and as a means of passing on the paternal wealth to the sons has never had a reason to exist. Moreover, the women of the proletariat have always worked.

The crisis of the bourgeois male of this century is a crisis of the absolute power of the man in the family.

The bourgeois male, no longer "King," suffers from so-called complexes and neuroses: it occasionally happens and with ever more frequency that the bourgeois woman works and it is then that the famous crisis of the male whose crown has been taken away occurs.

The vendetta of the detroned "King"

In Marxist countries neuroses no longer exist nor does the crisis of the male inasmuch as the entire society is changed economically and all the women and all the men are changed.

To the contrary here there exist couples of persons who try to live emancipatedly in a society that kills them. The ideal of the man socially remaining that of "King," an inferiority complex is born to all those who find themselves near women who are not their slaves. The conflict between the desire for a woman who is more than a slave and the traditional idea of the male as master leads the American, English, and Nordic in general, humanity to a new form of male vendetta that is *sadism.*

Sadists, I used to think, are those who suffer from particular sexual attitudes. But this sadism "*à la Sade*," French sadism, is nothing but eroticism. It has nothing to do with the particular sadism that is developing on an even larger scale in the souls of American, Swedish, or English men, and before long Italian men as well.

This sadism, today, they call "mental cruelty." In reality it is a slow and subtle form of killing one's woman and becoming "King" once again.

At the origin of this sadism there is the emancipation of the woman and the anguished position of the male before this phenomenon which completely destroys the idea of the capitalistic bourgeois marriage, with the man as absolute master.

Today in the Western countries one witnesses the breakdown of the capitalist marriage, in an economy that remains fundamentally the same. The spiritual, physical, and moral victims are this mass of neurotics, inhibited women, women living alone, suicides.

My dear friend committed suicide. But we all know that she had been slowly led to suicide, drop by drop.

She had been killed even before she killed herself. Suicides are not born other than on burnt terrain. The vendetta of the wounded male, wounded because of failure, led him to kill that which he loved. For years he told her, "I love you," and a month later he would say, "I don't love you any more." For years we have witnessed these excruciating scenes, the cause of which was nothing other than the crisis of the man of this century confronted with the woman who works.

And to think that he was in love with her! But making her suffer, having her at his feet, making her run through the night like a madwoman in search of him, Laura once again became the slave and he the "King."

VI

August on the Beach (I)

"What you said about Adam just now. I mean . . . if God hadn't felt sorry for him and created Eve, what would he have done?"

"What do you mean, what would he have done?"

"About his sex life, I mean. What kind of sex life do you think Adam had before God created Eve?"

"What the hell kind of crazy question is that? How am I supposed to know? Maybe he didn't have any sex life. Maybe he—"

"Do you think maybe he might have gone with the animals there in the Garden of Eden? Some people still do. Sheepherders, they say, are supposed to be freakish about sheep . . ."

"Look, Doris, this is turning out to be one hell of a picnic. First you drive me here to this deserted beach. Then right off the bat you insist we take our clothes off and lie here naked. Now this crazy idea pops into your head—"

"The reason I insisted we get naked right away is so you won't make a pass at me. I know you like me, but I don't want you to make a pass at me. I've got too much respect for your wife for that. By the way, does she know you're here?"

"No, and anyway it's none of your business one way or the other!"

"Christ! Are you writers sensitive! No wonder you're always writing about sex!"

"What's being sensitive have to do with writing about sex? And anyway I'm not a sensitive writer and there's very little sex in the things I write about!"

"Not even in the book you're writing about me?"

"Doris, you're a mess! And stop nursing that bottle. You've already had too much to drink . . ."

" 'You've already had too much to drink!' You sound just like that fucking count!"

"I wish you wouldn't use such language. It doesn't become you. After all, you're practically a countess . . ."

"Practically a countess, nothing! You don't have to rub it in. I know damn well what I am. A well-kept woman whose nightly assignment is to help our friend the Count get over his goddamned inferiority complex. Did I tell you, he finally got around to confessing what I already suspected—?"

"Confessed what?"

"Don't be so damned anxious. Do you want your notebook and pencil so you can write it all down before you forget it? What a bastard you are! The poor girl commits suicide out of love and you write it all down in your book and probably'll get rich and famous writing about other people's misery—!"

"If you don't want to tell me—"

"Tell you what?"

"You said the Count finally got around to confessing something—"

"That's right. He finally got around to confessing that he couldn't do it with white women, not even his wife. That's why he separated. It took me to bring out the beast in him. No kidding. That's just what he said, it took me to bring out the beast in him. And speaking of beasts, if you were Adam all alone there in the Garden of Eden, which animal would you have gone with?"

"Oh, I don't know. A cat, maybe—"

"A cat, small as they are? What would you do it with, your little finger?"

"Doris, you're perfectly obscene! If you keep on talking like that you're going to end up getting raped. And it would serve you right!"

"I'd have to tempt you with an apple from the tree of knowledge, and I don't see any apple trees around here. As a matter of fact, I don't see trees of any kind. This is one hell of a lonely place—"

"It's Etruscan country, those hills back there are full of Etruscan tombs—"

"I know, I know. You've told me so at least ten times. This is one hell of a country! If it's not catacombs, it's Etruscan tombs—"

"Italy is a land of many and diverse stratified civilizations—"

"Excuse me for interrupting, Professor Demby. But may I go to the bathroom, please?"

. . . "You looked just like Eve coming out of the bushes there just now. Suppose *you* were all alone in the Garden of Eden. What animal would *you* go with?"

"A horse, a nice shiny white horse!"

"I won't ask you the same question you asked me. But I can understand your choice. All down the ages, women have been sexually attracted to horses. And they're right. A horse is a wonderful symbol of beauty, power and speed. Qualities which most men lack—"

"Let's leave the Count out of this!"

"I wasn't thinking of the Count. I was speaking of men in general—"

"The Count likes dogs. He's got one that's almost as big as a pony. I hate the damned thing. Always jumping up on me from behind. Did you ever notice how our folks don't go in much for dogs?"

"Now that you mention it, I never thought of that before. Maybe it has something to do with dogs supposed to be man's best friend—faithful and all that, just like in the South white people used to think their slaves were faithful and loyal, like dogs are supposed to be. Or maybe it's because American Negroes have a subconscious aversion to dogs because they still remember the hound dogs that used to chase runaway slaves— Hey! Are you asleep?"

"No. I was just resting my eyes. It *is* peaceful here. How did you ever find such a beautiful deserted beach like this? Have you been here before?"

"I came here once before, about ten years ago. With my wife, before we got married—"

"Were you really in love with my mother, really in love? I mean, if all that hadn't happened between my mother and that so-called father of mine when you were in college together, do you think you and my mother might have gotten married? Or did you always want to marry a white girl? Some of our people are like that, you know—"

"Well, you can leave me out of that category. If I married my wife it was simply because I happened to be in Italy at the time, and I was in love with her!"

"More than you were in love with my mother?"

"That's an unfair question. For one thing, I was a lot younger then. It's different when you're a freshman in college and away from home for the first time in your life—"

"Do I look like my mother?"

"Fantastically so. Especially the eyes, the long arms, most of all the hands. They're soft and strong. I never saw your mother naked—"

"Come closer—"

"Is this close enough?"

"No. Closer. That's better. Take me in your arms. Let's pretend I'm my mother. Kiss me . . ."

("So, passing desperately from sleep to death, Marilyn Monroe has passed away: and the contrast between her famous milk-and-honey beauty and the final black beauty of death is too violent not to leave a strong impression on us . . ."—*Il Giorno*, August 6, 1962)

"What I feel most. Well, it's hard to put it. What I mean is, I feel there's a . . . there's a new kind of cleanness in the world. The opposite of meanness . . . Don't make fun of me. You writers are always making fun of people. Don't make fun of me, or I'll get sore as hell. And, if there was any raping done here on the beach, I did it. And don't you forget it, either. But what if Marilyn Monroe was a kind of Christ?"

"Doris! You're raving drunk!"

"Go put your goddamn pants on, and don't 'you're

raving drunk' me! I mean it! What's so funny about Marilyn Monroe being Christ? I mean she made people sit up and take notice. She made people *feel* something about women. You said so yourself—she's all over the papers and sneaking into people's minds. Making people think what a *woman* is. Not going to bed with a woman. You men know what a man is because you got Christ, or Adam crucified. But what about Eve? You can laugh all you want to. I'm religious, and I don't care who knows it. Marilyn Monroe got herself crucified so everybody'd start thinking what a woman is. I don't feel sorry for her. I revere her! You wait and see. She's going to be the fountainhead of a new religion. Marilynmonroe-anity! Christ, I am getting drunk. What time is it anyway?"

(OTHER SUICIDES AND ATTEMPTED SUICIDES FOR THE DEATH OF MARILYN MONROE. *Il Messaggero*, August 9, 1962: ". . . unfortunately the suicides or attempted suicides 'by imitation' continue. In just a few days a former actress in London, a former dancer and three teen-agers in San Francisco killed themselves. Yesterday a Mexican university student, Luis Miranda Villasenor, attempted suicide. Today there were two more suicides and two attempted suicides. A 43-year-old woman of Marioneth in Wales committed suicide by swallowing a hundred aspirin tablets, having been profoundly impressioned, according to her husband's statement, by news of Marilyn Monroe's death. The woman, Ella Owen, left a note in which she speaks of what she considers the affinity of her own life with that of the deceased actress, especially the unhappy childhood . . .")

"I never told you. But I knew her. I mean I met her once. With my sister in New York. At the première of *Rose Tattoo*. Marlon Brando and Tennessee Williams were there. She drank champagne out of my glass. She was in love with Arthur Miller. They were going to get married. She told me she wanted to come to Italy—"

"Please pass the bottle . . . Thank you, Sir Fauntleroy. Lord Count Fauntleroy . . . Yum yum, smack, smack! . . . What I mean is . . . was trying to say . . . I mean, most women hate Christ, hate the very guts of the . . . they even hate the *idea* of Christ . . . But now after Marilyn Monroe's sacrifice . . . Well, you know . . . We women can *identify!* I mean, for the first time in my life, I'm digging Christianity . . . I mean I'm digging Christ! Christ! Do women suffer . . . I mean, does everybody suffer? . . . A metaphor of Marilyn Monroe on the Cross . . ."

"You're crying. Maybe we better go back . . . Now, come on, Doris . . . You're spoiling everything. Why are you weeping . . . what are you *crying* about? Come on, get off it . . . People are committing suicide every day. Men and women. Think of Hemingway. Think of—"

"Oh shit! Go put your goddamn pants on! I'm fed up with acting out this Garden of Eden bit. Where did you learn to make love anyway? The way you make love is just like the Count makes love. With one eye and one ear always spying on me to see if I'm getting a thrill. Poor

Marilyn Monroe! She drank champagne out of your glass. I suppose you're going to make a note of that and put it in your book, like her husband was always making notes about her. Everybody was always making notes about her. Put all the notes together and what do you get—the apocryphal gospel of Marilynmonroe-anity! Look at the sun, it's falling into the drink . . . 'to me only with thine eyes . . .' What time is it getting to be? And for Christ's sake, go put your goddamn pants on. I don't want to see another naked man as long as I live!"

"Is that better? Do you want me to put on my shoes and shirt too?"

"There goes the sun. Oh, it's beautiful here. Listen to the birds. Like you could walk over the sea to where the sun just went down. Everything hushed up. You ever notice how when the sun goes down, everything slows down for a little while, everything becomes quiet? Sunsets make people want to die. Isn't it strange how people are usually sleeping when the sun comes up in the morning, but almost everybody stops what they're doing to watch a sunset. Like they're afraid of birth, the sun coming up. Like they're tempted by death. 'Oh, I hate to see, that evenin' sun go down . . .' Have you seen Laura's husband since the funeral?"

"No. Why?"

"I was just wondering. I feel kind of sorry for him . . . 'I hate to see, that evenin' sun go down . . .' I mean. If a white boy marries a pretty colored girl like that, you'd think—"

(73)

"Doris! You're talking like a goddamned fool! The fact that Laura happened to be a Negro doesn't put her automatically into a kind of elite immune from all the emotional stresses we're all subjected to! Aside from the fact—"

"Aside from the fact that she was a Negro, you're proud to say that one of our own happy high-dancing race had the moral courage to take her own life! Why don't you write an article about it for *Ebony* magazine? 'Another Negro First! Jamaican girl in existential suicide pact in Rome!' "

"If I were you, I'd go dress. It's getting cool. I think we better be heading back to Rome."

"Oh, no. Let's stay. This is Thursday and the Count has a staff meeting. Let's build a fire and stay!"

"Well go put your clothes on. I'm going back to the car to get that pack of cigarettes we left on the back seat—"

"Your wife won't mind? You're sure?"

"No, my wife won't mind. And stop using that sarcastic tone of voice every time you mention my wife!"

" 'Oh, I hate to see, that evenin' sun go down . . .' Oh, Roman woman, with her diamond rings . . . !"

"You sly bitch. Go put your clothes on . . ."

"A real Boy Scout fire! If you weren't already married, you're the kind of man I think I'd like to marry. You know how to make a fire. That's the trouble with living in Europe. All the nice Negro men you meet are either queer or already married to European women—"

(7 4)

"And all the nice Negro girls you meet are already living with counts!"

"There go the birds again! Oh, I could stay here forever! Just listen to the surf. Like a baby licking a plate clean—"

"That's what scares me—"

"What?"

"Everybody having poetic thoughts, everybody a writer—"

"Do you mind if I tell you something?"

"Go right ahead, High Priestess of the Marilyn Monroe Cult. Speak, Oracle. Speak—!"

"I think you've been in Europe too long . . ."

"Original! Original! An original thought! Someone says that to me at least once a month. What makes *you* think so?"

"The way you make love. Don't laugh. And take your hand off my knee. A woman can tell. You've damn sure been in Europe too long!"

"Was I laughing? I don't know whether to be flattered or not. I mean, in the avocation of love-making, I thought Europeans were tops—I *am* flattered. But aren't we doing an exaggerated amount of talking about sex this afternoon? It just occurred to me that in ancient Egypt, the priests of the temple wore jackal heads. A jackal is a kind of dog—"

"The reason I'm thinking so much about sex these days is because I have so much time on my hands—now that the Cleopatra film is finished. Here's something for your novel . . . This morning when I was waiting for you at Rosati's, a strange man sitting at the table next to mine, with a dog and a Chinese woman, asked me if I liked Dante and if I'd seen the performance of *Aïda* at the outdoor opera last night. He said there were three shiny white horses on the stage . . . He asked me if I liked Rome . . ."

"And what did you say—?"

"I said I liked it all right, but—"

"But what?"

"That's when you showed up . . . He gave me his card. He has an art gallery in New York. He deals in oriental art . . ."

("LAUNCHED BY THE RUSSIANS ANOTHER SPACESHIP THAT GLIDES SIDE BY SIDE WITH NICOLAJEV'S . . . The appointment on the orbit around the Earth . . . THE TWO PILOTS SEE EACH OTHER AND COMMUNICATE BETWEEN THEMSELVES . . . Total synchronism in the complex experiment, on the basis of high mathematical computations . . . Nicolajev has already surpassed all records for number of hours of flight and completed orbits: last night he slept, exploiting the method of conditioned reflexes coördinated . . . THE NEW ASTRONAUT IS NAMED POPOVIC"— *Stampa Sera*, Monday, August 13, 1962)

"Why do you think Pavlov used dogs for his conditioned reflex experiments instead of cats?"

"Why do they capture all those monkeys in India to export to American scientific laboratories?"

"Why did Arthur Miller make Marilyn Monroe act in that film about cowboys hunting wild stallions to sell to dog food factories?"

"Why does slavery still exist?"

August on the Beach (II)

(It is three minutes past midnight, August 15. The moon is full, a fierce white pendulum suspended over the quiet sea and restless clouds that swarm close to the earth like vaguely frightened lambs. The sand is warm. A breeze blows from the south and cools the perspiring skin as though an invisible swarm of moths were fluttering past. Eyelids flicker with sleep but are torn to wakefulness by the angry glare of the moon. The heavens are in tumult. Dogs howl in the distance . . . Headlights race along the foot of the hill. Stars are sprinkled densely over the floor of the sky like spotlighted grains of spilled salt. ASSUMPTION. Latin *assumere*, to take to. A festival in honor of the miraculous *translation* of the uncorrupted body of the Virgin Mary to heaven by Christ and His angels at her death, observed by the Roman Catholic and Eastern Orthodox churches on August 15. The Russian astronauts hear a sound like music, faint but near, there is a passing scent of perfume. How can we know we are moving, if there is no illusion of movement or passing of time? It is four minutes past midnight, August 15. Doris and I are still on the beach . . .)

"Why did you make me stay, Doris? We shouldn't have stayed—"

"Are you afraid?"

"Afraid of what? No. I don't think I'm afraid—"

"I know what you're thinking—that if women were more like Women, those Russian astronauts wouldn't have had their rendezvous in space—"

"That if men were more like Men, Marilyn Monroe wouldn't have committed suicide, the Virgin Mary wouldn't have been a virgin, wouldn't have been assumed into heaven by her Son—"

"What you say makes me afraid –"

"The words of what I said make me afraid. But here and now, here and now with you, I am not afraid, after the words have passed. Where are you going?"

"I'm afraid. The Count is waiting. I am afraid to face the Count. If only the moon would set. If only the astronauts would return to earth. If only I weren't afraid—"

"Afraid of what?"

"Afraid of—afraid of—afraid of— Afraid of I don't know what—"

"Feel that breeze? It must be blowing from the south. It cools the perspiring skin. As though an invisible swarm of moths were fluttering past."

"That's what I'm afraid of!"

"Afraid of what?"

"Everybody a writer, everybody having poetic thoughts!"

"Doris, what a bitch you are! As soon as I get home, I'm going to flush every page of this stupid novel down the toilet!"

"If you did, you wouldn't be a writer, you'd be a hero!"

"What do you mean by that?"

"Take your hands off me! I'm sick of hands and flesh! I'm sick of men—!"

"Now stop it! You stop that crying! You're getting hysterical—!"

"You're goddamn right I'm getting hysterical! Who wouldn't get hysterical making love with a goddamn writer, always spying on her to see what a thrill she's getting, always making notes?"

"You make me sound like a vampire or something!"

"You're worse than a vampire! You're a—you're an undertaker, that's what you are!"

"Doris! Now stop it! Stop that crying! You hear me? Stop that crying!"

"I want to go home—!"

"Stop crying, I say! Stop it or I'll—!"

"You sonuvabitch! You slapped me in the face! I'll—"

"Get hold of yourself! You're acting like a drunken slut!"

"I'll drunken slut you! Oh, why did I come here anyway! I hate this place! I hate Italy! I want to change my name—!"

September, the Quarrel, a Monologue (III)

Now, it is Saturday, the Saturday of September the eighth, Feast Day of the Sacred Nativity, Feast Day of Mary. (The Count is jealous; Doris has not come home yet, and it is nearly two-thirty in the morning; Doris is somewhere with that Sly American Negro Novelist who claims that he is writing a novel about her; the Sly American Negro Novelist is married to an Italian Girl of Good Class—then why must he *insidiare* my Doris? Doris! Doris! Come home to (this apartment that's costing me fifty-four thousand lire a month rent) your home, come home to your Count, who is pacing to and fro like a lion in a cage (Alice says that men chain smoke and pace to and fro like lions in a cage in maternity hospitals while their wives are screaming with the pains of birth out of guilt, out of a frustrated sense of wanting to share the suffering, which, of course, they cannot, until they, again out of guilt, suffer the pains of birth upon the symbolic Cross); the Count is jealous and ashamed.) And while he, like a lion in a cage, paces to and fro: "GOTHIC TALES' AUTHORESS ISAK DINESEN DIES AT 77. Copenhagen, Sept. 7 (AP)—Baroness Karen Blixen, the Danish authoress who became world famous under her pen name Isak Dinesen, died today, 77 years old. The cause of her death was not immediately known, but a member of her household, who refused to identify herself, confirmed that she had died. Under her pen name, Isak Dinesen, an adaptation of her birth name, she made her debut in world literature at the age of 49; but it was a spectacular debut that quickly carried the hawk-nosed baroness to world fame. That first book, *Seven Gothic Tales*, has found its way to more than a million bookshelves the world over since its publication in 1934. Ironically it was first written in English—which the baroness considered her second language. Several years later she translated it back into Danish and published it in her native country for the first time . . ." My wife translated Isak Dinesen's *Out of Africa* into Italian. Alex says: "What a pity that all the big game animals of Africa are disappearing . . ." I reply: "The Africans are poisoning them . . ." My wife, my son and I go to the beach on Procida and the water is gray and calm until there is a rocketlike disturbance, and a *merluzzo* chases a smaller fish almost to the pebbly shore where my son stands testing the temperature of the September surf: "*Guarda, guarda! C'è un pesce-cane!*" But it is not a *pescecane* but a *merluzzo* chasing a smaller fish. But the next day, in the Bay of Naples, the moon is full and freshly minted; as we return to Rome, the deadly gray steel of the atomic aircraft carrier, the *Enterprise*, anchored in the full moon—Vesuvius, Santa Lucia and mandolin fireworks, Bay of Naples: deadly gray steel. Jones, a friend whom I have not seen for thirteen years, comments and says to me and to my son and to all the September vacationers returning to their calendar rhythms, breakfast in bed: "Each one of those planes on the flight deck packs the power of twice the earthquake in Iran, it is the biggest most powerful vessel of all time, the American aircraft carrier, the *Enterprise* . . ." My wife is dismayed: "It is an instrument of death, each citizen is entitled to a seat on the train between Naples and Rome!" she says.

I look at the deadly gray steel and think: "It is beautiful, the power is under control!" Crisp in his freshly laundered uniform, a gigantic black American Negro sailor with aristocratic, kingly nonchalance shows his pass to the SP guard at the gate and saunters over to the waiting launch that will take him to the deadly beautiful steel shark-whale presiding over the full moon night of Naples, Pedigrotta and songs and the blood miracle of St. Gennaro. The train rocks and rushes through the night and immediately I am home after the short vacation, and I call Alex, and I say: "Alex, the *Enterprise*, the atomic aircraft carrier, is docked in the Bay of Naples!" And Alex, at 10:00 P.M. says, his tone condescending to better absorb the meaning of 10:00 P.M. intrusion: "In Naples? The Bay? I thought no one wanted the atomic aircraft carrier anchored in their bay—" It is there, and the moon is full; it is there, and the power contrived by man is terrible, but we shall not march with sloganed banners, but shall accept this power, because it is there, and we shall—? (The Count, as he paces to and fro, building up steam for the Terrible Quarrel which is about to take place here in this tiny apartment which he has rented for Doris, his mistress, thinks now of his sister who is a nun in the Congo; the Count thinks of his father who was an amateur explorer in Africa, his father who is dead while his sister, the nun, is alive.) In Iran, says the morning edition of *Il Giorno*, JACKALS AND VULTURES MASTERS OF VILLAGES LEVELED BY EARTHQUAKE. ("I'll huff and I'll puff and I'll blow your house down," says the Big Bad Wolf to Walt Disney . . . Says *Epoca:* "Before succumbing to the horrible wound, Maurizio Sarra, the champion lung diver killed by a shark in the waters off the coast of Circeo, shouted, 'Go away, cursed Death!' " *"This is the first photograph of the terrifying earthquake in Iran which appeared last Monday, September 3, in newspapers all over the world in which over 30,000 people lost their lives* . . . TOO MANY DEAD TO BE COUNTED.") (But now there stops a 600 Fiat beneath the window; the Count peers out as a jet plane rises impudently across the newly minted surface of the moon; it is Doris; and the Count huffs and puffs and applies make-up and slips into his costume and puts on a wig and rehearses before the bathroom mirror and wets his lips and turns on footlights and spits and stamps his foot and peeps out between the curtains and hushes the invisible audience: "Sssshh! The Terrible Quarrel is about to begin! . . ." Doris is climbing the cold marble steps to the small cold apartment the Count has rented for her. Her hair is mussed. She feels like a thief. She stops halfway up the stairs after the second-floor landing, where there is an open window that opens onto the courtyard and a junglelike garden and a palm tree with waxy green leaves thirsting greedily after the first cold rays of the morning sun; four cats like a gang of teen-agers stalk across the courtyard with their tails obscenely raised; looking out the window, out over the courtyard where from the checkerboard of open windows, on a warm summer day, maids and lonely housewives spy on the handsome plumber's apprentice and sometimes sing their songs of longing and loneliness, Doris takes a small mirror from her purse and a gold-enclosed tube of lip-stick and paints her pouting lips . . .) Thus, a minute becomes weeks, and today is September the twenty-first. I told Alex, at our last meeting, that I could not begin to write the quarrel between Doris and the Count until the weather changed, until the long-overdue summer storms broke this malevolent sun-crazed summer's spell. Sunday came the electromagnetic storms. Rain for vineyards, rain to wash the atomic radiation out of the air. T. has returned to Rome. Together we returned to the Circolo degli Artisti. Doris was there. Yes, I think this is the real Doris at last. She is a dancer. She was one of my partners on the TV program. I do not know her name, but she does indeed look and act like my invented Doris. The suicides and poisonings continue here in Italy. An Amer-ican lady, very rich and the wife of a gangster, commit-ted suicide in the Flora Hotel, and this morning's news-papers say that she was collaborating with the FBI to break up a gang of dope smugglers. A tornado struck Capri and Sperlonga and the island of Ischia; at the opening of an art exhibition, Sartoris', at Charles Moses' gallery, on the day of the tornado, Elsie Rieti tells me that she has just returned from Capri; Milly, who has just returned from Capri, has just given birth to a baby girl (and everyone said that she would die if she had another child!); Sperlonga is where my wife and I went on vacation while she was pregnant with our only child, and where Elsie Rieti and I were going to build a villa together; Ischia is where my wife worked on a film with L.B. while I was having a furtive affair with my young son's nurse on the island of Procida: only these three places were struck with the tornado. Then everyone got up to dance the Hully Gully. Mostly they were pale American Negroes, though our friend the Ethiopian ras was there in his waiter's disguise. And there was a terrifying sadness to this dance of the Hully Gully, the pale American Negroes (and "Doris") dancing a parody of minstrel joy: How sad this sight! I was in the last chapters of this novel and I had by chance come to the Circolo degli Artisti and seen Doris, months after she had been abandoned by the Count, and she was trapped in the very special sewers of Rome, the Catacombs, which this terrifying city reserves for rebelling slaves, and I wanted to save her—Doris, Doris! What are you doing here? Why haven't you called? And the puffy flour-faced clerk-intellectual who was revitalizing his contact with the world of the primitive looked at me strangely and asked: Who is he? And Doris said—she was drunk and ashamed, and T. was watching me with his Icelandic remoteness, an ironical smile on his face: He is a friend, he is a writer, you remember he was on that TV program I was on with Louis Armstrong and Sammy Davis . . . You know my name? "Doris" asks. I must save her, though we are not yet in those final chapters when all this is happening, and I return to the table where T. is waiting and say: We must save Doris before it is too late! And T. only laughs and says—rising as if on cue, and a few blond girls and wan young men doing this absurd Hully Gully dance, like drugged monkeys performing at a county fair on a hot rainy day: It is not true that we Negroes like to dance . . . Then why do we dance? Why do people close their eyes when they make love? . . . Doris blinks into the tiny mirror; someone opens a window overlooking the courtyard, the old naval officer who is about to die from insomnia this spring, who winks at Doris when he passes her on the stairs, and a look of hope comes into his eyes as if she can save him from the case of syphilis he contracted as a youth, fifty years before, after winking at a dark-skinned beauty in that Dakar port . . .

(Doris fumbles for her key, she opens the door: Why are the lights on? Immediately the Count appears at the end of the cold marble hall . . .

"Well?"

"Well what?"

"Tell me all about it—how did it go?"

"How did what go?"

"I happen to know that you spent all yesterday afternoon, and probably the night, with that Negro writer friend of yours. Is he *really* writing a novel about you? I mean, have you read any of the pages, touched them with your hands? Let me tell you something. No, I'm all right . . . You needn't look at me like that. No pills, no whiskey. I'm perfectly lucid. But I'm jealous. And the reason that I'm jealous is that I think that Negro writer friend of yours is vampirizing you . . . Why are you laughing?"

"That's what he—that's what Bill Demby said yesterday afternoon—that he was a vampire, that he was vampirizing me because he was writing a book about me. I mean, how can you vampirize someone just because you're writing a book about them? I mean, all men are vampires, all human beings are vampires, women too. After all, we're warm-blooded creatures aren't we? I mean, we need blood to live—and they don't sell blood in supermarkets. Not human blood anyway. They put ox blood in that sophisticated red wine everybody's talking about, they put ox blood in it to make it red. But that's ox blood, not warm human blood. And vampires want warm human blood, just like babies want warm human milk, and what is warm human blood but red-colored warm human milk, sophisticated fake mother's milk . . ."

"*Che stavo dicendo?* I'm not ashamed of being jealous. Three hours ago I said I'd kill you when you came home. That's what I said. I tried to get the Liston-Patterson fight on the radio. You should have heard what Higgins said about that fight. I think he knows about us. He said that American Negroes are weak because they have mixed blood. Liston is black as coal. He's a savage. Brute force. He said the fight was between Africans, real Africans, and namby-pansy American Negroes. Then he asked me something about us which I shan't refer to you. He wanted to know whether I was able to satisfy you. And when I said I thought you were perfectly satisfied with our relation, he laughed, and said our relation is just like the Patterson fight with that Swede, that if I really want some competition, if I really want to know where I stand as a man, I should go to Africa and take on a real African girl. I couldn't get the fight on the radio, but I see by the morning papers that Liston won. That Higgins is a Nazi. He thinks that the blacker you are or the whiter you are the better chance you have of winning. Doris, Doris—! I know I'm raving like an idiot, but this is the first time I've been jealous in my life—"

"And you're having one hell of a good time, aren't you?"

"Doris, don't be nasty . . . if it were anybody else, but one of your own race, and a writer too . . ."

"Well, what do you call yourself? Didn't you just ask me to tell you all about it? Why are you men always spying on women so? I mean, why can't you just simply accept the fact that women are—well, different? Here I am all alone in Rome, and the only two friends I have left—well, one wants to write a book about me, and my other friend, the one I'm supposed to be in love with, well he wants to know all about what went on when I'm with my friend who's writing a book about me. So where does that leave me? A kind of walking peep show! Hell, both of you want to know about what goes on when I'm with the other. Well, if *I* started to play the part of a writer? What if I made up things to tell you both? What if I started telling you both the things you *think* you want to hear? You say you're jealous for the first time in your life. Well, you know something? I think you're lying. You're not jealous. You're just working yourself up into one of those sneaky erotic moods. And if you want to know something else, I happen to know that you knew all along that I was going to Ladispoli with Bill Demby, and I—oh, what the hell's the use? I'm tired, I'm so tired . . ."

"Doris, don't cry . . . don't cry, Doris . . . it's all my fault, darling, I started all this . . . don't cry . . . Wait a minute, I'll phone Higgins at the office and tell him that I won't be in today. How's that? You go get some sleep, and when you wake up we'll go that restaurant on Via Appia Antica, you know the one? The one where the hunters came. The one across from the Catacombs. Here, darling . . . let me unbutton your . . . now lie down here . . . sleep . . . I'll sit right here until you wake up, then you can have a nice bath and we'll go to that restaurant on the Via Appia Antica, the one where the hunters came. The one across from the Catacombs . . ."

"I'm so tired . . . I want to change my name . . . how come the birds know before we do that the sun is about to rise? Good night, Sweet Prince . . ."

"Count, Doris . . . your Sweet Prince is only a Count . . . now try to get some sleep . . .")

October, the Concilio, a Dialogue (IV)

With solemn earthbound joy, October is drawing to a close. In our vineyard the new wine is fermenting. The moon cycles are violent; the earth trembles and absorbs mysterious energy from its magnetic core: is Autumn Birth or is Autumn Death? Now the Season of Time welds its circle, the Serpent swallows its tail. This is the season when the Moon is king; and ". . . RANGER 5 STARTS SUN ORBIT; MISSED MOON BY 350 MILES. Pasadena, Calif., Oct. 22 (AP)—Ranger 5 and its sightless television camera came within 350 miles of the moon Sunday, its builder announced. Then, the Jet Propulsion Laboratory said, the spacecraft curved past the moon's back side toward a probable orbit around the sun . . ."

"NEW LOOK FOR THE 'PIETA.' Vatican City, Oct. 22 (AP)—Michelangelo's 'Pietà,' one of the outstanding art treasures of the Vatican, has been shifted to give viewers a better look. It's the sixth time the statue, placed in St. Peter's in 1499, has been moved. Vatican art experts say this time the position will be closer to the one Michelangelo himself had in mind. The statue depicts Mary with the dead Christ lying across her knees. Since its last previous shifting in 1749, the 'Pietà' has stood in the first chapel to the left of the entrance of St. Peter's. Redig de Campos, a Catholic priest and art scholar, said in the Vatican newspaper *Osservatore Romano* yesterday that the way the statue had been placed before was an 'outrage' to Michelangelo's design. He said Michelangelo had wanted the figure of Mary leaning slightly to the *left*, whereas the old placing made the figure almost vertical. The 'Pietà' had been moved off its old pedestal in the chapel and placed about four feet lower, brought about three feet forward from the chapel wall and inclined slightly toward the viewer. The statue is slated to be shipped to America for the 1964 World's Fair at the request of Cardinal Francis Spellman . . ."

I have just returned from Paris where I met a man who, as S. tells me, is at least partly responsible for the analyzing of shipwrecks and the shipping of valuable cargoes by water from one port to the other. Last week, before, on sudden impulse, leaving for Paris, I was asked to write an introduction for the exhibition of a young Roman artist whose works have interested me and are in my collection, Losavio. This is the introduction I wrote:

Losavio

Does the sun's ray penetrate to the mother's womb where the drama of birth is taking place? Do the invisible rays of atomic radiation penetrate the stone and concrete shelter where Adam and Eve reënact the drama of Creation? Inanimate objects, be they tables or chairs, typewriters or pillows, Michelangelo's "Pietà," are formed of invisible universes of matter and energy: in this sense they are alive. Enclosed in a room, church or museum, house or castle, they influence one another—condition one another's existence (just as the "animate objects," the human members of a family, influence one another, condition one another's existence, in a house or in a castle). This is Losavio's discovery: my plastic dramas, dramas of Light and Space, must not be influenced by, conditioned by, other objects, "animate" or "inanimate," in the *place* where they shall come to *rest . . . locus, repose.* My plastic dramas, dramas of Birth and Creation, of Light and Space, must not be conditioned or influenced by any drama other than the drama of the movement of the sun: Even when you, the Spectator, shall walk all around the world I have created—even when you inarticulate Spectators, tables and chairs and other works of art, shall transmit your vibrations—my plastic dramas, my dramas of Birth and Creation, of Light and Space, shall unfold in a spatial silence of *my* fabrication. For I have enclosed them in a womb, a shelter; a womb and a shelter of crushed stone and cement.

William Demby

And the atomic aircraft carrier *Enterprise* is now in the pirate waters of the West Indies. And the morning newspapers cry "Wolf!" (A wise man indeed was

Aesop!): BLOCCO NAVALE A CUBA . . . U.S. BARS WEAPONS TO CUBA . . . LE NAVI CHE PORTINO ARMI SARANNO DIROTTATE . . . APPELLO A KRUSCEV PER MANTENERE LA PACE . . . 61 AFRICAN BISHOPS UNITE ON LITURGY . . . COUNCIL HARD ON POOR CLERGY . . . 18 YEARS FOR BRITISH ADMIRALTY SPY . . . "SOLD HIS COUNTRY FOR CASH" . . . FATHER OF DEFECTING SOLDIER WANTS A "FACE TO FACE" TALK . . . 7 DIE FROM SMALLPOX IN JAKARTA, INDONESIA . . . CHINA ADVANCE BRINGS NEHRU FREEDOM SPEECH . . . ITALIAN PLATOON IN THE TYROL AMBUSHED, 1 WOUNDED . . . REDS LEAVE UN MEETING OVER CHINA . . . ARTIFICIAL INSEMINATORS THREATEN TO STRIKE . . .

Aristophane!

Today is Saturday, October 21, 1962, and I am in Paris . . . But before I go to Paris, where I have already been, I must face a fundamental technical and philosophical problem. When I began this novel, I secretly decided that, though I would exercise a strict selection of the facts to write down, be they "fictional" facts or "true" facts taken from newspapers or directly observed events from my own life, once I had written something down I would neither edit nor censor it (myself). The novel must be like a plum cake: while baking a plum cake or after it is baked one does not remove a raisin or a nut just because one doesn't approve of the way it has occupied a choice site or moved too close to another raisin or nut. Novels, in theory, anyway, are supposed to be slices of life, slices of plum cake. So once the cook has created and stirred up the mixture he has no moral right or obligation to censor, or select: all the cook-writer can do is taste and smell and say "Yum-yum" or "This stinks!"

So before I go to Paris where I have already been (Today is October 30, war over Cuba has been miraculously averted, the Concilio proceeds, three Fathers have died, the African bishops want to know, as problems of liturgy assume increasing and perhaps fundamental importance, why the Devil is black and angels are white, an English writer and his wife who in Kenya had been threatened by the Mau Mau were mysteriously murdered in Sardegna where they had planned to buy a piece of land) I must bring forth these pages of September 27 which I illegally suppressed:

The Quarrel begins:

He says:——!!!

She says:——!!!!!

He says:——!

She says:——!

He says: ——!!!!!!

She says:——

(The World says, the Chroniclers say: Today is September 27. I have insured my life for five million lire, and the policy is enclosed in imitation embossed leather, red, with the *stemma* of those Venetian financial thieves and pirates embossed in imitation gold on the cover. If I die I shall receive five million lire; on the other hand, if I live I shall receive 430 thousand lire per year at the age of sixty; all are embarrassed at the Idea of death and politely make the sign of the horns, though, by recent statistics at the International Bureau of Statistics, it has been worked out by the prescient IBM computers that ten out of ten of all human beings die. Thus, as my favorite House of Hollywood, Paramount, says: *Non Giuocate Con Palline.* Alex, always ready with a *motto buono*, says: "Why *palline?*" He's thinking of course of the huge balls on the equestrian fire- and Vulcan-cast statues of bronze in our monumental piazzas here in Rome. As yet nobody knows what the Penelope threads of this tale are being woven into; and, for that matter, nobody knows, today September 27, 1962, who or what is Ulysses and who or what is Penelope, and who is doing the weaving, who is being woven, *pazienza.* But, to get down to brass tacks, and not gold-plated tacks, today is September 27, 1962, and here I have a fat envelope from T. containing the following journalistic information:

Now I shall be truthful, and this is fatal for a Writer, as John O'Hara would say, and as all Writers, feeling a strange unusual comical kind of comic-strip guilt—when some lines above I said "International Bureau of Statistics," what I really meant to say, as a "Pro" Writer, was "International Bureau of Slapstickstiks"—S. just called and said she is going back to Paris; apparently she did not finish her book about her erotic adventures in Nigeria—or Nigers—the African, Polish (Afro-Polo) Queen—with the President—or, as my son would say, "*Console*"—of that Negro land—How "readers" must have a hard time following "writers," but "That's *Life-*

Time, time, always time—LIFE"—now where was I? Oh yes: Now I shall be truthful. But then you people will say that this is not Fiction, you PEOPLE will ask: "Where are the REAL CHARACTERS?" Well, as a starter, what about me, the Author? I mean, "Ain't I every bit as interesting as Doris or the Count?" Oh, but you are not a *fictional* character! Well, and today I am in a playful—or as my loving wife would say, a Mozartian—mood—I goddamn well feel like a fictional character. Which reminds me of what I was about to say: I'm sick of the news again, I have *mal di giornalismo* . . . I don't believe anything that I read, even what T. just sent me: GERALD BLAIN APPARTIENE ALL' OAS? SAINT PETER'S BOMBED!! FOOD FRAUD SCANDAL SHAKES GOVERNMENT . . . WINE MADE OUT OF CEMETERY BONES . . .

Christmas is coming, the goose is getting fat,
Please put a penny in the poor man's hat.
Three Letters (V)

Today is November 8. *Il Giornale d'Italia,* in its page-one editorial, has finally discovered that "intellectuals," scientists, artists and poets, are engaged in warfare, the new warfare of ideas. But so it has always been. If only we had a uniform, and medals instead of money prizes. Ribbons to wear on our hats. Symbolic swords instead of typewriters (how happy I was to see a news photograph of John Steinbeck, who had just won the Nobel Prize for literature, seated behind an IBM typewriter like mine, which, with the quietly efficient hum of its electric motor, has always given me the feeling of power of sitting at the controls of some advanced model of a Sherman tank). Yes, as the angry editorial in *Il Giornale d'Italia* says: "It is the most monstrous of wars because it is fought in the name of peace. It is a war which carries with it an extraordinary power of degradation. The old wars killed. This war is a demagogical mystification: it poisons and destroys the consciences. There are no dead but the death of the animus of the people, of the nation, is wanted . . ."

But we are at war. And, uniforms or not, we must fight. Is not the man who wrote this editorial an intellectual? Then why does he prefer that other kind of war, which is much easier? Does the sun's ray penetrate to the mother's womb where the drama of birth is taking place? Do the invisible rays of atomic radiation penetrate the stone and concrete shelter where Adam and Eve reënact the drama of Creation? . . .

On February 27, 1956, John Steinbeck wrote me in the flyleaf of a new edition of the Shorter Oxford Dictionary: "Dear Bill—This is the mother of writers. It will make you feel small as it does me, but it will also lift you up. You can add to its greatness as so many of our craft have, but you cannot take away from it. This is no dead compilation but a living-growing changing organism—sparkling with the creativeness of the only creative species. May you add to its luster and may it suckle you—there is no finer thing than you and this book in harness together. Never forget that—'In the beginning was the WORD.' Your friend, John"

But today is November 8, 1962, and I read in this week's issue of *Time* magazine: " 'This is a radical step in what I hope is the right direction,' explained Crooner Pat Boone, 28, heretofore always the Mr. Clean of the movie business. Hoping to do right by doing wrong, Boone plays the heavy in 7 Arts' *The Main Attraction*. He is knocked silly in a barroom brawl and revived by Chianti wine spilled over his head by a circus floozy. He sleeps in her wagon (Won't there be talk?), later stabs her husband, runs away, is seduced by a bareback rider. Where on earth went all of Pat's on-screen morality? 'I have stepped out of the groove,' he said. 'In my first six movies I played myself. From now on I don't care if I play a derelict or a drug addict, just so the movie has a worthwhile message.' "

In *Momento-Sera* I read: "Robert Weaver, Jr., son of Robert C. Weaver, killed himself shooting himself in the forehead with a pistol. Robert C. Weaver is the American Negro who has reached the highest government position ever obtained by a member of his race in America, having been nominated administrator of the Federal Housing Commission. According to the police Weaver's adopted son had no intention of committing suicide but had been playing at 'Russian roulette' . . . etc., etc."

As I write, the kitten of the house which, so Emma claims, is the daughter of the tomcat given me last Christmas by Virduzzo's wife, and which committed suicide a day or so before that black Saturday when war was to have broken out over Cuba (at 7:00 P.M. I came running into the house announcing that Peace had broken out: no one believed me, but it was true!), gazes at me with tender amusement . . .

And now: "Christmas is coming, the goose is getting fat, who will put a penny in the poor man's hat?"

Doris' Letter to Her Mother, November 12

Dear Barbara, dear Mother—I started to write you last Thursday because I thought last Thursday was Thanksgiving Day. I started to send you some flowers too. I tell you this because it just goes to show you how detached I have become from America. Forgetting when Thanksgiving Day is! The Pilgrim Fathers shooting wild turkeys and making friends with the Indians they would later hunt just like they hunted the wild turkeys. Then when they got to be fat and prosperous and self-right-eous they would hunt whales and transport Negro slaves! This is the kind of thinking you do here in Rome. I mean, here in Rome you get a historical perspective about things, you take the long view of history but you can't find out anything about your own place in current history. At least I can't and I've been in Rome now for almost a year.

Don't get scared if this letter sounds the way it does, because one thing about Rome is that there's nobody to talk to or with. Everybody does a lot of talking but nobody talks to or with anybody, everybody talks to himself. That's why, out of sheer desparation, and also because I'm menstruating and a little bit depressed, I'm writing this kind of letter to you. I know. I should be telling you the facts—how I'm getting along, what I'm doing, if I'm meeting any interesting people, my work —I'm not working. I stopped dancing long ago, when work on Cleopatra ended (and what a blown-up phony experience that was, worse even than what the newspapers said, like the Last Days of Pompeii or something, no kidding it was weird. Once Elizabeth Taylor spoke to me. She asked me if I knew Ronnie Lenton. Now who in the hell is Ronnie Lenton? Before I could answer she had already walked away). In other words I have been out of work since May. How have I been living? Well, I see no reason why I shouldn't tell you the truth. After all I'm my father's daughter! I'm living with a Count. He keeps me. In short, I'm a kept woman in Rome. Well, now that I've finally told you I feel a lot better. So if you wait until I shower and change into something more comfortable, I'll continue this letter which shows every sign of becoming one of those long literary confessions that friend of yours, Bill Demby, says disturbed people should write to put things in their true perspective. I'll be back in a jiffy . . . (What a character *he* is! Bill Demby I mean) Hold on! . . .

Here I am again. I've just had a shower and a nice long drink . . . I needed the drink because here in Rome I've lost the habit of honesty, and, mainly for my own sake, I *do* want to be honest in this letter. In every letter you've asked me about Bill Demby, what he's doing, how he is. And in all the letters I've written you I've put off telling you—well, because up to now I haven't been able to make up my mind. For one thing, I don't think you would recognize him any more. I mean, he's not the Bill Demby you knew in college. It's not that he's "gone native," become Italian in his way of thinking, or in the way he thinks or acts. It's—well, he's kind of weird. For one thing—and hold your hat, mummy-doll!!—he's writing a novel about *me*, of all people! But if you ask me, I'm the one who should be writing a novel about *him*. The drink is beginning to take effect so I might as well tell you that *I think Bill Demby is beginning to fall in love with me!* Now I'll probably never mail this letter, but anyway that's just what I think. But you needn't worry, mummy-doll. If it's true he's beginning to fall in love with me, it's only in a kind of abstract literary sort of way—and, forgive me for saying so, I just bet that's the way he was in love with you. I think now I understand. He's a writer, probably he was born a writer. And that's what's so weird about him. What I mean is—it's as if he lives all by himself inside a chic luxurious apartment he rents inside one of his eyeballs, probably his left eye, but that's a private Roman joke, and I don't feel like filling you in on Roman folklore and superstitions right now (no kidding, it's worse than Harlem or Africa the way these Italians are superstitious about almost everything!). Maybe that's why Bill Demby is so weird. I mean he thought he was coming to a highly civilized country in Europe and suddenly discovered that in reality he was back in a kind of Africa his grandmother from Pittsburgh had tried to make him forget! Anyway, he's nice, but he's weird. And meeting him, and knowing him, has made me suddenly want to know and meet my father, the gangster! Now I know I'm not going to send this letter! Anyway, I'm starting to have fun—and I bet Bill Demby doesn't have fun like this, I mean writing down just any old thing that pops into his head (Say, this therapy is beginning to work! I'm beginning to feel good!).

Now where was I? I just took a nap and I had a dream. Let me see, it's two-thirty in the morning. What I dreamed was this: I was in line with a lot of Italian girlscouts. I didn't know what they were in line for at first. Then I realized they were going to kiss the ring of that African Cardinal, I forget now what his name is, but anyway he's the first African Cardinal in the history of the Catholic Church and he's here in Rome for the Concilio. Well, when it was my turn to kiss his ring, instead of kissing his ring I threw my arms around his neck and kissed him on the mouth, real sexy like. And you can well imagine how he, the Cardinal, reacted—his eyeballs popped out and he half stood up and said, "You're a disgrace to your race!" Then he called the Vatican guards and they dragged me away, and just before I woke up the Pope shook his head sadly and I think I heard him saying something like, "My daughter, you should not have done that!" The African Cardinal's name is Cardinal Rugambwa—I just saw a picture of him in a magazine sitting on a throne and a lot of schoolgirls standing in line waiting to kiss his ring. I guess that's where I got the idea for the dream.

There's something very strange about this Concilio here in Rome. I didn't even know it was going on until Bill Demby told me he got up at four o'clock in the morning the day it started to go to St. Peter's to pray. That's what I mean when I say he's weird—he does strange things like that. He said that on his way home he stopped at a café for an espresso and the newsboys were saying to each other, laughing and all excited, that the appocolypse (excuse the spelling, I don't feel like looking it up in the dictionary) was at hand. Another thing he did that's very strange is that he got drunk the day everybody thought war was going to break out over Cuba and when I called him up about seven o'clock in the evening, because my friend the Count had just called to tell me that if as was almost certain war was going to break out I should have my things packed and that we would go to his villa (it's really a castle but he doesn't like to call it that, no kidding!) in the country—when I called up Bill Demby to ask him what I should do and what he was going to do, he laughed and said (this is just what he said in his own words): "Barbara Baby, if you were here I'd give you a kiss—don't you know Peace has just broken out!" How did he know? Anyway, that night on TV I found out he was right. You see what I mean, about his being weird I mean?

But getting back to this Concilio. Bill Demby says it's one of the most important things that has happened in modern history (in Rome that's all you think about—it's always tombs and ruins and the long view of history, and frankly I'm getting fed up with the long view of history, otherwise Rome would be charming and champagne-fluffy like Paris, but I guess they can't help it, what with all the roads leading here and all the dead people fertilizing the soil and all the tombs honeycombing underground so much that they can't even build a decent subway system!). I guess he knows what he's talking about—do you know he reads something like ten or fifteen newspapers every day! Weird, really weird! Maybe it's a good thing you didn't marry him after all. Are you still in love with *him?* He told me all about your romance at college. But it sounds like something out of medieval history. I just can't imagine you two together (by the way, will you send me that snapshot you have—I know you have it, because I saw it in the bottom of that Valentine box of chocolates, hidden underneath all those corny letters Bill Demby wrote you during the war—of my father? I want to study it myself and I want to show it to the Count—he's fascinated by the idea that there are Negro gangsters in America and that one of them is my father!!).

The funny thing about this Concilio is that they're talking about race relations so much. But not only race relations between colored people and white people (apart from the African Cardinal, they made a South American colored man a saint and they're thinking of using Negro spirituals and tom toms in the celebration of the mass) but race relations between men and women. For example, they never mention Jesus' father's name in the mass. Now they're going to put him on the same level with Mary. If you know Italy, that's really something! And come to think of it, that's why I want my father's picture—*maybe!* There go the birds! It's almost dawn. Oh, mother, how I wish you were here! How I hate these menstruating blues!

I've just read what I've written so far. I didn't mean to talk so much about Bill Demby. I really meant to talk about myself and my friend, the Count. (Ever since Bill Demby told me he was writing a novel about me, I haven't been able to act natural—I mean, it's as if somehow he's taken possession of my mind and is around and invisible even when he's not: if he wasn't the only American Negro in Rome worth knowing, I mean the only one who gives me a kind of connection with my home and my past, I swear I'd never speak to him again!) Well, no more about Bill Demby—I know you're just dying to know about the Count whose "mistress" (doesn't that sound European?)—whose mistress I've become.

The funny thing about the Count (his name is Raffaele della Porta) is that Bill Demby introduced me to him at a cocktail party for the opening of an art exhibit at a gallery run by an old friend of his, an old friend of Bill Demby's. Later on I found out that Bill Demby had just met the Count himself but when I came in the door, trying to act sophisticated because it was the first art exhibit I had ever been to in my life and everybody looked like they were posing for one of those whisky ads in the New Yorker, they were chatting away like old friends—something to do with German expressionism (that's another thing that's weird about Bill Demby—he buys and collects crazy modern paintings that look to me like something straight out of an adult education class in an insane asylum!). You see what I mean? Here I am supposed to be talking about the Count and instead Bill Demby comes popping into the picture! Now wouldn't that be weird—I mean, if I were falling in love with Bill Demby. Excuse me (I was only joking!!) but this calls for another drink.

Now where was I? Oh yes, the Count. Well anyway the Count and I seemed to hit it off right away. He said his sister was a nun in the Congo and that his father had been a famous explorer in Ethiopia and Kenya. Frankly, I didn't appreciate all that talking about Africa and Africans, but I was so glad to be talking with anybody (and he speaks perfectly charming English) that I played along with him and tried to put on my best African queen act (I had to do the same thing once before in college with a refugee professor, but that's another story —these Europeans all have a one track mind when it comes to us colored women—they expect us all to be African queens or kings!!).

VII

Under the Sign of Venus, a Prophecy

Now is Venus warm to the cold helmsman's eye. The
sea heaves methodically, the time pudding boils. Consciousness drifts upward and is blocked by virgin mist:
human consciousness in vain tries to penetrate those mirror gases concealing that which is not. Tuesday, January
20, 1963, a beam of Telstar ionized hail reflects flicker-

ingly a packaged glimpse of The Gioconda Smile. Leonardo laughs as Lazarus laughed: "What *is*, can *become*, *is* and *is not*, on what side of the looking glass are *you?*" Venus' earthly ambassador is not André Malraux, but Hitler's bastard son, exiled from Italy though Kennedy shall come: KENNEDY A ROMA ENTRO L'ANNO—CALOROSO (angry is the sea, and lusty Europe for several weeks now has been wearing woolen undies and tongue-shined mink—COLD WAVE TO CONTINUE FOR ANOTHER MONTH BRITISH METEOROLOGISTS CLAIM—café chatter of colors, temperature, bees and honey, spiders, dwarfs, the stairs of St. Peter's, stairs leading to the vaults, stairs leading to the sun-peeking hole, the obelisk shipped from Egypt and erected in St. Peter's square by a crazy heretic proconsul Gaul, a stubborn blaze smoldered through the 102-story Empire State Building, the sex secretion perfume of 8,000 moths drives caged male moths mad and causes them to perform indecent acts among themselves, no babies born, silk and leather, wool and soap, Chamberlain of the Secret Chamber, Boy Bishop, Magistrate of Dwarfs, cancer, one last fling with boy-meets-girl-let's-run-off-to-the-SUNLAND-Sicily-or-Waikiki-Beach, throw him to the sharks; and this I said to my wife before going to sleep: UNLESS HUMAN BEINGS, DESCENDED FROM ONE MONKEY OR DIFFERENT MONKEYS, GESTURES OR INTELLIGIBLE SPEECH, LEARN TO SPEAK TO FISH AND ANIMALS AND POSSIBLY *creatures* OR *beings* OR *anti*-BODIES FROM *outer* AND *inner* SPACE, THEY HAVE LITTLE CHANCE OF SURVIVING THE RACE, THE HUMAN

Oh, Venus, Queen of Heaven, from my gaol, from the
tiny window of my skull-domed jail, I ask, I ask, I ask, I
must know: Oh, Venus, Queen of Heaven, why are you
hot in the evening and cold at dawn?

". . .On the planet of Venus, the existence of living
beings is possible. The study of the data transmitted by
the American satellite 'Mariner II' which passed the
planet at a distance of about 32 thousand kilometers confirmed this thesis. This revelation was made indirectly by
the observation of the extreme weakness of the magnetic
field of Venus, which would confirm the thesis according to which the 250 degrees centigrade of temperature
registered by the terrestrial instruments did not refer to
the planet's surface, but to the ionosphere which sur-
rounds it. With certainty, however, little is known, and
it is still a mystery what is hidden beneath the thick
curtain of clouds which are wrapped around the planet
Venus . . . *Vita, Settimanale di Notizie, Anno V—Vol.
IX—N. 195—10 Gennaio* 1963."

Now is Venus cold to the warm helmsman's eye. As
dawn approaches, the sea turns on its side and struggles to
hold onto the dream, slowly consciousness returns to
earth, penetrates the mirror warmth of flesh, consciousness worms its way like a vampirish virus into the mirror
warmth of Doris and the Count who sleep side by side,
in a bed, a vast acreage of a hotel bed, a matrimonial
hotel bed of *due piazze;* lumped under three thick blan-

kets, they lie back to back, their bodies now registering exactly the same temperature, tail to forgotten tail Doris and the Count have become Siamese twins, side to side, back to back, they hibernate here in this modern sunland hotel with modern warm-tiled bath, shower hot and cold (needles of delight or solace), in this luxurious government-subsidized (Casa del Mezzogiorno) hotel with no other guests, the waiters having long since shipped out as deckhands, able-bodied seamen, cabin stewards and assistant cooks; the service is slack but unobtrusive (the fluttering-handed proprietor's wife apologetically still does not know where the fuse box is), the water in the bathroom is vulcanically hot but dense with rust: back to back, forgotten tail to forgotten tail, lie Doris and the Count, here in this resort hotel on the island of Procida where, after two disparate nights in the unheated fisherman's cottage I loaned them, they have come to take refuge, have come to hibernate, to hole up like Alex's moles. Here it is warm, they sleep well and deep, and with dawn comes sunlight, for the first time in a week: stealthily the sun's ray touches a human-forgotten nerve on the rose-green underside of Doris' mascaraed eyelid, a curtain closed but open on a baroque spectacle of dream. Immediately she is awake . . .

I am awake (Doris thinks, says), I am awake, where am I, what day is today? The Count, we had octopus stew for dinner, nightmare, I found a pile of stolen silverware on Marilyn Monroe's grave, the Count is asleep sweet prince, only a count, oh! the sun's come out, the

Count needs a blond haircut, smells like red wine and milk, hotel on prison island Procida, buy linen bed sheets cheap handmade by prisoners, no women wives home, wives prisoners in kitchens, husbands weaving sheets like Penelope, life imprisonment, husbands wives everybody "in for life," till death do us part, prisoners selling immaculate linen sheets for matrimonial bed, first night flags of stabbed virginity like Japanese flag, prisoners snickering, selling immaculate first night sheets to summer tourists, "young couples," "in for life," flag or no flag, probably about quarter to eight, sun out for the first time in a week, don't wake up yet, asleep sweet prince, sheets cool as a diamond on this side of the bed ...

So let's try to figure it out mathematically; this really is one hell of a mess: today is Monday, January 22, 1963. On Christmas Eve, December 24, 1962, or was it December 25, I mean, as I remember, it was almost or after midnight, the Count rang the doorbell and said he was putting off going home for Christmas until the next morning because he couldn't bear the idea of me spending Christmas Eve all by myself, I was waiting for the operator to put my call through to New York, I wanted to say Merry Christmas to my mother, he had a bottle of champagne, he cried a little bit and we sang Christmas carols, *Silent Night*, said he wanted to marry me, come what may (me a countess!), anyway we made serious down-to-earth matrimonial love with the TV set on and a midnight Mass, Catholic, blaring crooning words in Latin, and a bell rang, on the floor, then I guess it was

December 25 after all, Christmas Day, I mean, if it was a midnight Mass on the TV . . .

The Count gave me a gold cigarette lighter for a present and left to catch the eight-thirty train, so I slept until noon, then I called Bill Demby, and he came over about, let's see, I think it was about six, he gave me two avocado pears for a present, dark oily green skins, never ate them, shriveled up like Mexican mummies, souvenirs of the worst mistake, technically speaking, I see you haven't lost your sense of humor, you better not, not after what you let yourself in for, no kidding this really is one hell of a mess . . .

Bill Demby came over about six, may as well be truthful, I phoned and asked him to come over, washed my hair, washed my undies, started a letter, opened a can of sardines, put on a Modugno record, nothing worked, Christmas Day in Rome wouldn't pass, moved like sticky syrup on a piece of toast, so anyway I asked Bill Demby to come over and he came, half stewed, said Christmas Day was his birthday, but nobody gave him any birthday presents except a hospital blanket and a cake of soap, Christ!, a fellow Nigra-American all alone in Rome, so *he* started singing Negro spirituals, he had a pint of Jack Daniels which together we gently and slowly drank, tears poured down his eyes as on Christmas Day in Rome 1962 he said only the Pope can save the world and sang ". . . Sometimes I feel like a motherless child, a long way from home," we ended up in bed from seven-thirty to eight-thirty when he had to go home because his son's electric train transformer had burnt out because the transformer . . . something about too much current flowing into the house, and his wife and mother-in-law always calling strange electricians, he wouldn't be surprised if the house was electronically bugged, thinks they think he's a secret agent, but he's not, just a motherless child a long way from home, so we made love, serious down-to-earth matrimonial love, what a Christmas I carry within my womb, what a Christmas present, don't cast pearls before swine, so that makes me a swine, carrying within my womb the seed pearls of two no-good-lousy-sentimental fakers, and where does that leave me?

What I mean is, the maiden's dilemma is simply this: today is January 22, 1963, according to the lunar calendar by which such things are regulated, I should start menstruating today, and if I don't? What if I'm pregnant? What I mean is, how am I going to know who the father is? "Yellow, brown and black and white, all are precious in his sight . . ." so they taught us in Sunday school, but what do you want to bet it doesn't work out like that in real life? For example: if I tell Bill Demby I'm pregnant and ask his help—I don't want an abortion after what happened to whatshername, I don't even want to think of an abortion, they'll kill me, I know they will, I don't want to die, and even if I lived I'd be dead, after what happened to whatshername!—and I go ahead and have the baby and the baby turns out to be blond and blue-eyed? What a mess! And if I tell the Count I'm pregnant and he insists on getting married, all happy and fatherly and family proud, and the baby turns out to be chocolate brown! What a mess, what a mess, what a mess! Well, lunar month or Gregorian calendar, we're all lunatics, I don't want to think about it, a nice hot bath, cheer up Doris my girl! A nice hot bath, that's what we'll do when the Count wakes up, we'll go up to the prison and buy some nice white itchy linen sheets made by the gentle hands of, maybe murderers, maybe cannibalistic Italian sex fiends, rapers of baby girls, we're all in for life, for better or for worse, a nice hot bath for poor Doris who has the dilemma of the century to solve, let's give the little girl a nice big hand! . . .

As they approach the prison at the top of the hill, a shapeless stone fortress that brutally assaults the eye lulled by quaint cobblestoned streets and the effeminate millinery shop, pastel pinks and blues of the houses and walls, Doris is suddenly afraid. Never before in her life, as in this moment (a cold wind blows up crazily from the muddy gray sea, beady suspicious eyes imbedded like dried currants in cold-shriveled faces stare at the haughty brown-faced girl, at her mink coat, the mink coat given her mother by her gangster father which arrived by air-mail parcel post a week before Christmas and which still smells of mothballs; a priest, a transparent arthritic image in dirty white and whitened black, stops in his tracks, takes a few steps backward toward the entrance of a tobacco shop, and surreptitiously crosses himself as Doris passes arm in arm with the tall blond count, a disembodied voice afloat on a pale green pamphlet announcing a religious festival in honor of the Marriage of the Holy Virgin says: *"Sarà un'attrice . . ."*) has she felt so far from home . . .

The Count heads sportively into the bitter cold wind, tosses the long end of his bright red cashmere scarf over his left shoulder, and says, as if talking to himself: "People who live on islands are crazy!"

Why are we here and now going toward that nightmarish castle to buy bed sheets and linen woven by prisoners, the horizontal threads a curse, the vertical threads a prayer? Are all white people living on an island? Are all white people crazy? What would the Count say if I told him I was pregnant and didn't know whether the father was black or white?

"You see, Doris, islands are not what they seem to be . . . Islands are cursed places. They are all that remains above water after unspeakable geological disasters. Islands are for hermits, for political exiles and dangerous criminals. The trouble with Procida is that plain ordinary bourgeois people are fooling themselves that they can live a normal life on an island like this. Procida is a place for prisoners, as all islands are . . ."

Doris is thinking: The end of James Baldwin's article in the *New Yorker*, how did it go now? "If we do not now dare everything, the fulfillment of that prophecy, re-created from the Bible in song by a slave, is upon us: GOD GAVE NOAH THE RAINBOW SIGN, NO MORE WATER, THE FIRE NEXT TIME!"

Does the Count *know*, Doris wonders, does the Count *understand?* ". . . *motherless child, a long way from home* . . ."

Tears come to Doris' eyes: the bitter icy wind, the mink coat given her mother by her gangster father, Bill Demby writing a book about her because he doesn't dare write a book about himself, the Count living on an island and calling islanders crazy, Doris hears distant music, organs and harps, a double flute, that dream she had about stolen silverware on Marilyn Monroe's grave . . . The bitter wind shifts with razor cunning as they enter the prison square . . .

A ghostly face peers down at Doris and the Count from behind a barred window over the entrance . . .

The Count, his clear blue eyes vacant, is saying: "*Ergastolani* . . . When I was learning English, I could never understand why there was no similar word for life prisoners . . . the nearest thing in English, and I can still remember what the Oxford dictionary said, was the word *Ergot:* a fungus, *Claviceps purpurea*, in color dark violet, in form resembling a cock's spur . . . the extra useless finger on a lion's claw . . ."

"Raffaele . . . let's go back to the hotel!"

"But I thought you wanted to buy some sheets and linen . . ."

"I did . . . I mean, I thought I did . . . It was really Bill Demby's idea . . . When he gave me the keys to that fisherman's cottage he rents, he said 'Be sure to go to the prison and buy some of the sheets and linen the prisoners weave to sell to tourists' . . ."

"Well? Isn't that just what we are about to do?"

"Let's go back to the hotel, let's go back to Rome . . . Isn't there somewhere in Italy where it's sunny and nice and warm?"

"Doris, darling . . . you make it sound as though I were responsible for this cold wave! Don't you believe me when I say it hasn't been this cold in Italy for over a century?"

"That's just the trouble! I *do* believe you . . . and that's why I'm afraid . . . First all that rain, day after day, week after week, and now all this cold, everywhere, even in Sicily, all over Europe, the canals in Venice are frozen up . . . Something strange is going on, it's a warning, God is warning us that another Ice Age could come . . . Two by two . . ."

"Two by two what . . . ?"

"Noah's Ark . . ."

"Doris! . . ."

"Did I tell you about the dream I had of finding a pile of stolen silverware on Marilyn Monroe's grave?"

"Sometimes, Doris . . . I mean, maybe the Church was right not translating the Bible . . . You say you're religious, but you sound like . . . I don't know what!"

"What if there *was* another Noah's Ark . . . Two of

each kind, you and me maybe . . . A space ship . . . We'd go to Venus . . ."

"But you said the canals were frozen over, even there . . ."

"Not Venice in Italy . . . the planet Venus . . . Two of each kind, you and me and Bill Demby and baby makes three . . ."

"Are you sure you feel well, Doris?"

". . . the space ship would sail through the mists . . . There would be a rainbow . . . Then the Captain would open the portholes, and we would see . . ."

"See what, Doris?"

There is a rumble of rotund thunder and a momentary flickering of lightning where the bottom strata of fluffy black clouds delineates a horizon with the sea that is false . . .

"What are you staring at, Doris? . . . See what? . . ."

"Don't make fun of me, Raffaele . . . Please don't make fun of me! . . . Take me back to the hotel, I want to go back to Rome . . ."

A Week of Crisis: THE FUTURE OF EUROPE AT STAKE . . .

Like a whispered blessing, snow for the first time in years falls on Rome. This is the last day of January, January 31. All during this troubled month, until this morning at 2:00 A.M. the snow began to fall, the doors of twin-faced Janus' temple banged open and shut with each shifting of the cold violent wind. As yet, there is no sign of spring: until this morning when the snow began to fall, twin-faced Janus, looking forward in time and back, wore the sinister dark glasses of the gangster and the celestial-tinted contact lenses of the saint. Boil, boil, toil and trouble: the time caldron bubbles, the fumes of alchemical transformation cloud the apprentice's vision. On this final day of Janus' reign, all speak quietly of the falling of the snow, all withhold judgment and wait. The looking glass our symbol. Helplessly we look on as the green-masked movers load our furniture onto the moving van. The looking glass our symbol, we dream of reinventing reality, we straddle time and space as all around the visible and invisible clash. Helplessly, as the green-masked movers load our furniture onto the moving van, only this do we know: that journalists and critics no longer rule. Social workers have forgotten what the word "social" means, hospitals are no longer hospitable, human man waits to be cured. And he shall (be cured): of the invisible and indivisible virus of madness (i.e., we grope in darkness but as yet do not touch) that attacks plants and animals, attacks that which is created and hence divine. Infants die before learning the mystery of speech, playful speech-trained dolphins freeze to death (sea cows, warm-blooded mammals; I remember the resurrection of the goldfish frozen in our backyard pond that coldest of winters in Pittsburgh, Pa.).

Our Father, who is in Heaven, may the crumbs of reality that fall from Thine Heavenly Table . . . we hungrily stick out our tongues: we admit humbly now that You are the Host and we the guests. We are not afraid, we are afraid to pray: our words are limp, the sun-drinking leaves of the African palms in the courtyard of our apartment building droop like the frosty Adamic appendage of an aged Moorish prince. Oh, God, Our Father, who is in Heaven, it is cold, it is cold, the white (European) world is cold, the flowers of narcissus bloom in the Himalayan alps (When will the marguerite bloom?). Oh, God, Our Father, who is in Heaven, it is cold, it is cold, the white (European) world is cold; cold the silly refrigerating thrill of cocaine, warm the God-ordained pillow of snow. Cool the color of money, crisp the rag-contented paper, warm to the touch. Technicians: wear white gloves that *pure* uranium and graphite (also waiters and maids) remain uncontaminated by human heat and sweat. Our Father, who is in Heaven, I am ashamed: white is not purity, contact lenses though they be tinted celestial do not necessarily make a saint. Hungrily we stick out our tongues (snowflakes cannot be hoarded nor placed on exhibition though each is a cameo of perfection). Oh, it is cold, the Caucasian world is cold, here in Europe now begins the year of perils: "Yellow, brown and black and white, all are precious in His sight!" Alex phones to say that in China this is the Year of the Rabbit. What does Alex mean? That the sexual-demographical disorder of the Chinese is a threat of some kind, is he referring to the "rabbit test" for determining pregnancy which Doris this morning has just taken; or is he referring to the fact that—?

In the meantime, Higgins smugly lights his pipe and blows a cloud over the morning's headlines (THE FUTURE OF EUROPE AT STAKE) and says, as though he has just invented the steam engine: "The sly silly bastard!"

And the Count, who is reading a copy of the same newspaper, looks up and says: "De Gaulle—a bastard? The trouble, I'd say, is that De Gaulle is legitimate, *purtroppo* legitimate . . . He is also very very tall!"

The Count is thinking: "Higgins is nervous, we're all nervous, something is going on that the papers do not tell us about, the Germans and the French sabotaging the Common Market like that, I must finish that letter to Maria Novella (what if Doris had to go back to America?), history changing under our feet, some of us will wake up one of these mornings suddenly old and out-moded, keep up with the times (but how?), something going on that the papers do not tell us about . . . this headline, for example: 'THE FUTURE OF EUROPE AT STAKE . . .' "

Suddenly the Count gets up and heads for the door: "Hold down the fort, will you Higgins . . . I've got to make a private telephone call . . ."

Higgins suppresses a smile and picks up a copy of the *Rome Daily American:* "Righto!" he says, and glances at the headline: MAC RAPS DE GAULLE BID TO RULE EUROPE. (Is "Mac" Macbeth?)

VIII

The Season of the German Rabbit

I sit this morning in the Café Canova, where Alex and I
have our weekly meetings, waiting for Doris to come.
Though I have been living in Europe for over one third
of my life, sitting in a café so early in the morning,
reading a newspaper, waiting for a girl, on a workday,
still fills me with a vague sense of discomfort, a feeling of

guilt: I am a schoolboy playing hookey from school; if only I could assume the purposeful air of the professional actors, striding purposely to and fro over the carpets, nervously and purposefully rushing from the men's room to the telephone booths, anxiously awaiting the single snowflake of gossip from TV headquarters on the third floor Heaven above . . .

"Peek-a-boo! Come out from behind that newspaper, Herr Wilhelm, here I am . . ."

". . . and you're late! Sit down over there where I can look you straight in the eye . . . You're more than half an hour late, forty-two minutes late, to be exact, and why, may I ask, 'Herr Wilhelm'?"

"Tell me. Have you ever had a problem, I mean a *real* problem, like . . ."

"With what?"

"With the problem, the *real* problem . . . like what you've never had one of . . . Von Steuben, our elderly waiter friend in the red coat, is coming—the redcoats are coming, everybody's taking up sides for the final Revolutionary Battle . . . The young waiter is wearing a green coat, Sherwood Forest and all that . . . No white-coated waiters in *this* café! . . . Do you come here often?"

"My friend Alex and I used to have our weekly chapter-reading meetings in Rugantino's café . . . Rugantino, an eighteenth-century Roman slum hero who drank too much and talked even more, ended up in prison, though when Alex and I used to meet there, there were a lot of pretty girls coming in, two by two, one wearing green, the other wearing red . . . Lately I've started making my appointments here, but I hadn't noticed that the waiters . . . some of them wear red coats, the others green . . . *Strange . . .*"

"Everything is strange and mysterious to you, that's because you writers don't have any *real* problems . . . What did you say the name of this café was again? It damn sure is velvety warm and comfortable in here, a home away from home, a Viennese coffee house without newspapers . . . *Zeitung!*"

"This café is called Canova . . .you saw the movie *Imperial Venus*, with Lollobrigida acting out the part of Paolina Borghese? This used to be part of the Hotel Russie . . . The Italian Television occupies most of the building now . . ."

"Please, no more history if you don't mind . . . Give Von Steuben here our order and get it over with . . . I've got problems, *real* problems . . ."

("*Due espressi, per favore . . .*"

"*Si, signore . . .*")

"*Si signore* . . . How does he know you're a *signore?* . . . Well, we'll let that one pass . . . Now just answer my second question first: How come the waiters in this café don't wear white coats, how come some wear red coats and some wear green coats . . . The Red and the Green: I guess that has something to do with Life and Literature . . . Stendhal, maybe . . ."

"You're referring to *The Red and the Black*, Doris . . ."

"Black and White, you mean! . . ."

"I beg your pardon?"

"Black and White: this *real* (now isn't that a weird coincidence . . . *real, reale* in Italian; *royal* . . . dynasties and dinosaurs, and all that jazz! . . .) . . . what I was saying was that this *real* problem of mine has to do with Black and White . . ."

("*Tragica Fine di una Nobildonna. La principessa Daria Borghese muore in un incidente stradale. La nobildonna, consorte dell'ex-comandante della X-mas, viaggiava su una 600 Fiat che si è schiantata contro il rimorchio di un pesante autotreno dei pressi di Teano . . .*")

". . . Where Garibaldi and the King, Vittorio Immanuele I, met! . . .

("*Lo sciopero nazionale dei medici verrà revocato se il disegno di legge sulle tariffe sarà approvato oggi . . .*")

"Will you please stop stealing glances at the *Messaggero* or whatever the hell that cheap newspaper's called? I'm in trouble, I tell you! I've got *real* problems . . . and believe me they're not the problems of the world!"

"All right . . . all right . . . let's have it! . . ."

"The German rabbit has spaken! . . ."

"Yes?"

"The German rabbit has spaken: the doctor says I'm *really* (ha! ha! *royally!*) pregnant this time, no doubts about it! The German rabbit—God rest his fertile soul —has spaken!"

"Spaken to who . . . spoken to whom? Our conversations keep getting sillier and sillier! I think it's time you go back where you came from . . ."

"Spaken to the German woman gynecologist at the American Hospital: she says I'm pregnant beyond doubt . . ."

(" *Grazie . . . e anche un bicchiere d'acqua . . .*"

"*Si, signore . . .*")

"Now, Doris, calm down, stop raising your voice . . . *Ciao!*"

"Who was that?"

"Parella . . . he makes *avant-garde* documentaries . . . a good friend of Marion Rosselli's whose father was shot down by the Fascists across the river from where I live . . . No, that's Matteotti . . . anyway, her father was shot down by Fascists . . ."

"The Count was laughing about somebody here in Rome whose little finger was shot down by Fascists!"

"Seriously, Doris—and be quite frank with me, if only out of respect for your mother—Am *I* the proud and happy father?"

(Almost five minutes pass: my mother in Washington snaps off the bedlamp and tries to recapture the scrambled image of the dream; my brother in San Francisco switches off the late movie and says to Natalie, his wife: "I'm going to bed . . ."; La Pira, in Florence, steals a glance at his watch and sighs; the raging core of the sun turns over one-ten-millionth of a degree . . .)

"No . . . this happened three weeks *before* Christmas . . ."

"Then—?"

"If mortal man has made me pregnant . . . then that mortal man is the Count!"

CASTA DIVA: *"Does the sun's ray penetrate to the mother's womb where the drama of birth is taking place?"*

At dinner last night I became very annoyed, if not homicidally angry, with my mother-in-law because she said that not only do I talk too much but that when I talk it is impossible for anyone to understand what I am saying because my "thoughts" wander at a rhythm impossible for anyone to follow from one subject to the other, illogically. Greta Garbo was on TV, in *Queen Christina*, and I became annoyed with her too; mainly because, I think, she wears dark sunglasses and is what I have come to call a "Casta Diva," though she is anything but divine, since after all these years she continues to cling with Swedish tenacity to the vine of her myth, like one of those shriveled-up grapes, at least one of which you will find in any vineyard months after the more human grapes have been harvested. So I left my wife, my mother-in-law, the nurse and my son (who having just joined the Boy Scouts is studying to earn a merit badge in How To Make the Harem Ladies Laugh and Why) to suffer through the glacial agonies of the Divine Greta—how many women of a certain age and generation dream of sitting on a throne and wearing black pants and a white cavalier collar while a nervous gray eminence in black pants and a white cavalier collar announces in a dramatically modulated drama-school tone of voice that ten thousand men have been killed in the latest queen-instigated battle! . . . I retired to my den with its double bed which only our pregnant cat seems to want to share with me (she has dreams, and whimpers petulantly in her sleep, and looks at me accusingly when I get up to go to the bathroom at three o'clock in the morning, looks at me accusingly as if I had committed a terrible crime by disturbing her dreams, looks at me accusingly as I were the one who had made her pregnant, which just goes to show that women are all alike whether they're Casta Divas, queen bees, silly pregnant cats, mothers and mother-in-laws: I don't think that women like men very much, but I like Doris, and now that she is pregnant, I am determined to protect her, she needs my help, and I am going to be helpful) and listened to my favorite Louis Armstrong record, and I listened to, and carefully read the libretto of (La Callas singing the female lead) a very fine recording of Rossini's *Il Turco in Italia.*

But today is Wednesday, February 13, and in the latest copy of *Time, hot* off the newsstands, I read this bit of *cool* news:

INDUSTRY

. . . People have always tried to find ways to prevent birth, from the froth collected from the mouths of camels in ancient Egypt to the clumsy rubber devices for men that accounted for most contraceptive sales in the U.S. until the late 1930s. About that time Margaret Sanger started the trend toward contraceptives for women by convincing major companies that there was money to be made in jellies and diaphragms; in World War II, the men's side of the business profited mightily from Armed Services educational campaigns. Today the major emphasis is on a recent development that has made contraceptives for women the biggest part of the business and promises to transform the entire industry: *birth control tablets . . .*

Somehow I feel devilish today (no doubt yesterday's badly suppressed anger against the pregnant cat, my mother-in-law and the Divine Greta is partly responsible), and the devilish thought has just come to me: What if some devilish Tycoon of Industry with a limp, a cape, a cane and a devilish look in his eyes has duped the ladies by passing off just plain pink sugar and glucose placebo pills as "GUARANTEED TO PREVENT LIFE OR YOUR MONEY BACK 'OBSCURANTISTIC BRAND BIRTH CONTROL TABLETS' . . . Have Fun Without Fear Like Cats and the South Sea Natives!" "Be Divine Without Dropping from the Vine!" (This is an unpaid advertisement for . . . "The contraceptive industry's outlook is for ever greater business. International concern over the population explosion, a free and easier society, and promotional efforts to instruct the public in family planning have diminished much of the opposition. Drug manufacturers believe that they have tapped only 20 percent of the market for contraceptives. They expect to reach much of the rest with new, cheaper and more convenient products. Oddly enough, they also count on a population that is steadily rising, despite their efforts, to give them new customers . . .")

What a strange expression "population *explosion*" (the action of going off with a loud noise, or bursting, under the influence of suddenly developed *internal* energy); an atomic reactor becomes *critical*, a patient in a hospital is placed on the *critical* (constituting or relating to a point at which some action, property or condition passes over into another) list; The Tibetan Book of the Dead says: "THE THIRD METHOD OF CLOSING THE WOMB DOOR . . . Still, if it be not closed even by that, and thou findest thyself ready to enter the womb, the third method of repelling attachment and repulsion is hereby shown unto thee: There are four kinds of birth: birth by egg, birth by womb, super-normal birth, and birth by heat and moisture. Amongst these four, birth by egg and birth by womb agree in character. As above said, the visions of males and females in union will appear. If, at that time, one entereth into the womb through the feelings of attachment and repulsion, one may be born either as a horse, a fowl, a dog, or a human being . . ."

The visions of males and females in union . . .

That afternoon on the beach of Ladispoli Doris said: "You writers are always spying on us women when you make love to us, to see if we're getting a thrill . . ."

Is Doris really pregnant? Can birth be controlled? Can weather be controlled? Albertus Magnus had two particularly famous pupils—Thomas Aquinas (1225-74) of Italy and Roger Bacon (1214-94) of England. Bacon became an active alchemist. He popularized Jabir the Arab's notion concerning the principles of "mercury" and "sulfur" (Hermes and Lucifer?). Some have credited Bacon with inventing gunpowder, but it now seems that the first European to make gunpowder was a German alchemist named Berthold Schwarz.

Today is Saturday, February 16: yesterday a cold needlelike rain fell; in the afternoon I went to the Auditorio in Via della Concilazione to hear a very rare performance of Rossini's 'La Petite Messe Solennelle' which he wrote shortly before his death; it is not altogether solemn, but there is a moment of glory when tears of joy came to my eyes; this morning's headlines are strange, are calm but urgent: ASIAN FLU ARRIVING FROM GERMANY . . . FIFTEEN THOUSAND CASES IN INNSBRUCK . . . VACCINATION WINE AND COGNAC THE BEST CURE . . . URANIUM EN ROUTE VIA TRUCKTRAIN TO ROME . . . ARMY UNDER ACCUSATION AFTER DE GAULLE ASSASSINATION ATTEMPT FAILS . . . HUSBANDS IN STATE OF ALARM! . . . THE "REVOLUTION OF WOMEN" AT CONGRESS OF MAGISTRATES . . . WOMEN ASKING FOR: RIGHT TO MAINTAIN OWN NAME AFTER MARRIAGE, REDUCTION OF "EXCESSIVE AUTHORITY" OF HUSBAND AND RIGHT TO BE QUALIFIED AS HEAD OF FAMILY, ABOLITION OF DOWRY . . .)

(Can there be such a phenomenon as a "population explosion"?)

Today spring has come and suddenly now I have a

vision: a drop of water issues miraculously from a mountain rock, the drops of water become streams, the streams become rivers, the rivers flow south (though "south" be "north"), away, away from the possessive magnetic clutch of the male—south, ever south, flow the rivers of the world, south to the solemn green silence of the swampland mating ground, to that windless acre where Birth takes place, where the fresh-water innocence of the rivers of the world makes union with the timeless Father-Mother thirst of the salt-weighted sea . . .

"Pacem In Terris"

("POPE STRESSES PEACE IN EASTER MESSAGE. Vatican City, April 13, 1963 (AP)—Holy Saturday services were offered in Roman Catholic churches around the world today as the end of Lent and the joyous celebration of Easter draws near. A highlight of the day was Pope John XXIII's scheduled annual Easter message to the world scheduled for 8 P.M. Rome time. Vatican sources said he would discuss his new encyclical 'Pacem In Terris'—Peace On Earth—and express the view that its call for universal peace would be his Easter gift to the world . . . In the St. Peter's service and in Roman Catholic churches everywhere, candles are lit at the church doors to symbolize that the light of the world—Christ—still lives even though his body is buried . . .") ("UN ANNUNZIO UFFICIALE DELLA 'CASA BIANCA'—*La signora Kennedy attende un bimbo per il mese di agosto. La* 'First Lady' *ha cancellato tutti gli impegni pubblici e pertanto non accompagnerà in giugno il Presidente nel suo viaggio in Italia* . . ." *Il Messaggero,* Tuesday, April 16, 1963.)

Today is Tuesday, April 16, 1963: the gray winter witches have left Rome at last, they have passed silently through their secret tunnel under the Alps, a dried-up underground river strewn with diamonds that do not glitter because there is no light, back to their summer abode on the other side of the leaden mirror, back to their rusty-iron-nailed, invisible abode, atop a magic mountain where magic moments dematerialize into demagnetized dance floors where dancing couples of gray lifeless winter ghosts strive in vain to recall and assume the preordained patterns of the Volta-directed quadrille —one, two, three, four . . . bow and curtsy! . . . Positive here! Negative *there!* . . . One, two, four, three, one, two . . . all in vain, the gray winter witches have left Rome, in vain they thirst for iron, desperately they seek to recall the preordained patterns, the four-sided pattern of rock-crystal perfection, dancing their three-numbered quadrille, the gray winter witches hibernate in their lightless heatless waterless ironless spa in Hussite Bohemia, praise be the Lord of Light, we are granted a reprieve, warm shines the sun on this *chiesa* which is Rome, projecting both warmth and light on microscopic vegetal consciousnesses colonizing the alfresco painted hands of saints, warming the brazen birth button of that first naked Venus, goddess immaculate, madonna without clothes . . .

This is a dark depressing time for the novel, a strangely critical time in my life. It is a Janus-time of looking back and forward, looking forward toward Birth, looking backward toward Death. In the meantime I am weightless and suspended: I can eat, sleep, urinate and shit in this weightless suspended condition. But suddenly the mirror has clouded, I have no knowledge of myself. Out of desperation, I thrust the manuscript on my friend Giancarlo Vigorelli, and another copy I send to my agent, Martha Winston, in New York. Why? Though I am in serious financial difficulties, I did not send the manuscript to my agent hoping that she would sell it—since, obviously, it is by no means "finished." The real reason, I think, is that I am undergoing a crisis of fear. I am moving over a landscape of time and reality totally unlike the dream world I had been living in up to now. These trees and mountains, these rivers and strange fish, these utensils and flowers, these streets and noises are unfamiliar to me. I am here and *there* . . . and now, saying this, I am no longer afraid, nor do I feel *divided*. Yes, now I understand what is going on: I am like so many others of my generation (I am not exceptional, my soul wears a gray flannel suit—but my underwear is plastic, flameproof, fire-engine red), I am a commuter

. . . In the morning I go to "work," in the evening I return home to my wife and son, even though I have not moved. Commuters we are, nor should we be ashamed!

But it is spring and I would like to laugh and be happy, I would like to flirt with the pretty green-legged girls, would like to touch their revolutionary breasts. But something of that *other place*, something about the *office* where I spend my work hours, remains impressed on the retinas of my eyes . . . and their inviting smiles fade. They are right: even I do not love myself, though I do respect and admire this Wilhelm man who has stepped out of his place in line and strides purposely backward, passing outraged twitching noses and scandalized eyes, toward the memory of a pool, something forgotten in the billion-year-ago past, something having to do with un-catalogued sea creatures suddenly appearing on beaches, their blubbery flesh stinking in the summer heat, terrifying photographers, reminding bikini-teen-age flesh that perhaps Birth is not Sex, that even though perfumed, Sex like Birth does indeed persist! *Orchestrine* play on the Lidos of the world, summer waiters dream of becoming dukes, white gloves touch the decaying flesh of (not the teen-age-bikini-capsuled flesh) the mysterious uncatalogued dying sea creature suddenly appearing on the beach . . . while I, the only one present able to translate the codelike whistles and corklike grunts, torn cold with love and recognition as the creature's "words" take shape: "I have reached the shore, I have come home at last, you human creatures should forget the sea, why must I, a stinking rotting dying fish creature, have to remind you? Learn to love this shore, this earth, this *land*—forget the sea (you are not fish, you are men—and women)!"

. . . and now three weeks have passed, and here I am standing on these silk-smooth stones of St. Peter's square, gazing up at the window of the dying Pope. Five years ago I stood in almost the exact spot gazing up at the chimney waiting for the puff of white smoke that would announce to the world that a new pope had been chosen at last. It is noon this Pentecost Sunday. Again it begins to rain (and always always there comes this gift of soft menstrual rain to embroider this unfinished tapestry of timeless changeless change) and Sheila Walsh, a freckled girl reporter for the United Press, sidles up to me for a spot interview. "What do you think of it all?" she asks. "What do you mean 'What do I think of it?'" "The scene, everything—" I do not think she is satisfied with my muttered reply. I told her that I was a writer myself, and that for the moment I am in no mood for writing. Finally she goes off to interview someone else, and again I am alone with my thoughts (the shame and guilt and anger of these weeks for those terrifying newspix from Birmingham of fierce gum-chewing police dogs enforcing the Law with Nazi efficiency!) gazing up at the window of the dying Pope, wondering why I am here . . .

Today I read in the papers that the Pope's last words were: *"Mater Mea . . ."*

This morning, like ants among ants streaming in an endless flow toward some unexpected morsel of edible flesh, my wife, my son and I join the enormous crowd entering St. Peter's to pay homage to the now tiny Pope encased in stiffly foldless garments of red and gold embroidered silk. From a distance, towered over by the colossal marble presence of St. Peter, the *statue*, Giovanni XXIII looks like a gift-wrapped gourmand's *caseus* (an ashen-faced distraught woman tries to throw herself down on the floor to pray, to rape that body of the Everyman who is dead, there is a swift black flutter behind the wooden barrier and a plainclothes policeman says loudly, in the dialect of the Italian south: "Keep moving lady, *circolare, circolare!*"). And as slowly, like boarders in some enormous *pensione* shuffling through a drafty corridor in bathrobe and slippers, we move with uneasy unaccustomed reverence through the deceptive time-space dimensions of this *chiesa* which is Rome, the plainclothes policeman's words remain impressed on my mind like a chiseled phrase from the dead Pope's encyclical . . .

"Circolare, circolare, keep moving—this is no time to stop the forward movement of souls!"

Impulsively the fat mustached barber bends over the Count and holds up a mirror and the Count becomes three. *"Va bene così?"* the fat mustached barber says, and suddenly it begins to rain (again the soft lawn-quiet rain, the warm menstruating rain, and Doris, sitting on a bench in Villa Borghese, remembers a ball game her father took her to, Satchel Page, the Pittsburgh Crawfords; she smiles and, after taking another glance at the headlines—BIG 3 PLAN N-TEST BAN TALKS IN MOSCOW . . . NO CONFLICT AS 2 NEGROES ENTER 'BAMA . . . KENNEDY INSPIRED BY 'PEACE ON EARTH' ENCYCLICAL FOR TOUGH SPEECH TO NATION—as on that day, carefully folds the newspaper into a child's soldier hat, and places it jauntily on her head . . .), momentarily creating an illusion of calm and peace on the street, and the fat mustached barber's girlishly plump fingers shift the mirror to the other hand, and he turns toward the door, and for a few moments his free hand remains poised, like a radar screen courteously admonishing some playful invisible intrusion . . .

(OMNIS HOMO AD VITAM NATUS
OMNIS HOMO AD MORTEM NATUS
OMNIS HOMO AD NATIVITATIS NATUS
AMOR ANGELI SANAT . . .)

Nervously the Count shifts his weight in the leather-and enamel-trussed barber chair throne. Always these weekly meetings with his wife have been an ordeal for him, but today more so than ever: just an hour or so before Doris had told him that he, not Bill Demby, is the father of the child she is expecting in August . . .

"*Va bene così?*" the fat mustached barber repeats, surreptitiously scratching his crotch.

Suddenly, outside, there comes the dull hamletical thump and the sprinkling of broken glass of an automobile crash on the corner . . .

"*Va bene così?*" the fat mustached barber repeats, changing the angle of the mirror, the angle of vision . . .

And at once a swiftly opportunistic gust of wind sweeps through the door and sends the soft balls of the Count's shorn lavender-blond hair gliding over the imitation marble floor of the barber shop like thistledown over a bleak mountain ledge . . .

(And now, as the noon whistle sounds and first Lillian Johnson and then my friend Alex phone, I return to the typewriter with a strange question on my mind: "Who is Hamlet, what is a hamlet, is not a hamlet a tiny village without a church? . . .")

Habemus Papam

The maid opens the door wider and lets him in . . .

"*Buon giorno, Signor Conte* . . ." she says, her tiny kitchen-work eyes blinking myopically behind steel-rimmed glasses as abruptly she turns off her duty-inspired smile . . .

The Count glances at himself in the full-length mirror to the right of the door, but instead finds himself observing the dark varnished reflection of St. Jerome and the lion in the desert: the painting badly needs restoring, there is no smell of cooking in the house, the walls need plastering, why is the maid looking at me like that? . . . BLACKS AND WHITES CLASH IN MISSISSIPPI . . . probably saw it on TV last night, police dogs, now that I'm not here in the house it wears a plaid skirt instead of a maid's uniform, no smell of cooking in the house, now what does that mean? . . . "*La signora sta nel salone . . .*" The subtle emphasis on *signora* brings a cool flash of resentment to his cheeks . . . does she know, Marozia, the cook and maidservant who has been with his wife from the day they returned from their honeymoon, about his affair with the American Negro girl, Doris?

"*Grazia, Marozia . . . Il figlio sta bene?*"

"*Benissimo . . . Gl'anno offerto un posto al cotonificio quando esce . . .*"

"*Ciao, Raffaele . . . come stai?*"

"*Bene, grazie, e tu?*"

Like a patient abbess (she is of ivory complexion, raven-haired, her figure is full, weighted to this earth, but there is an ethereal lightness to her glance, like a thirty-jet monster military troop carrier designed by a madman who has only known the embraces of teen-age whores, about to make the, all know, impossible effort of taking off, she looks like a Jewess, loved by William Breakspeare in a Shakespearian PLAY, this is Adelaide of a noble family traumatized in the Italian south by northern blondes and southern brunettes, dashing about with TV purposefulness looking for the hidden Easter eggs in those days of the Crusades, the Holy Chalice Grail safely hid in Switzerland, bank secret box number . . .) of a strange new convent, as yet without orders, but a convent where there is no smell of cooking in the house, Adelaide, legitimate wife of the Count, looks up from her newspaper (*Momento Sera* of Tuesday, June 18: NELLA SISTINA 82 TRONETTI IN UNO DI ESSI IL NUOVO PAPA) on the inside pages of which are *Variety* magazine actor-type photographs of all the Cardinals, all the Princes of the Church who in two or three days, a puff of huff and puff and I'll blow your house down smoke, one shall be pope . . .

"Has it stopped raining?"

"Yes, the sun is shining now. Why do you sit in darkness?"

"I was looking at the pictures of the Cardinals. Marozia and I have been playing a game. Each of us has three choices. We put our choices in three different colored boxes. One red, one black, one white . . ."

"And which Cardinals have you chosen?"

"We swore not to tell . . ."

The Count laughs uneasily and begins knocking his knees together.

"Does one of the Cardinals of your choice have a beard?"

Adelaide laughs and touches her shiny black hair.

"What a devil you are? Why do you ask that?"

"Speaking of devils . . . there is a Negro Cardinal . . ."

"Marozia keeps a picture of him in her sewing box . . . I saw it the other day when I was looking for a spool of white thread. She tore it from a newspaper and keeps it with a picture of Saint Antonio of Padua, and a snapshot of her son who is in jail . . ."

"Yes, she told me. He is to be released soon. She said they have offered him a job in a cotton mill. That was a stupid thing to steal that antique plate . . . it wasn't even gold . . ."

"Let's not talk about Roberto. Let's talk about you. Marozia says you have a Negro mistress . . . Now don't be angry with her. She hears these things at the market, so all Rome must know. Is she beautiful? Perhaps we shall have a Negro pope . . ."

The Count laughs and folds his long hands over his stomach.

"First of all, the Negro Cardinal's name begins with 'R' and he has no beard . . . He has practically no chance of becoming pope. The best he can hope for is that he doesn't get a stomach ache here in Rome. The Romans have started thinking they're Romans again . . ."

"Are you hungry?"

"As a matter of fact I am. But I don't smell any cooking from the kitchen. What do you two live on these days? Alka Seltzer and rose petals?"

"Oh, you remember? How long ago that was!"

(In a cave deep under the ground the needlelike point of a stalagmite breaks off, then silence returns . . .)

"I do have a Negro mistress, Adelaide. She is pregnant. In August she will have my child . . ."

Marozia enters the room with suspicious swiftness . . .

"E' pronto! . . ."

"We're having caviar and smoked salmon and champagne, and there will be candles, and you will call your office and tell them that you are tied up . . . and we shall talk and talk and talk until we have elected ourselves a pope . . ."

Marozia hands her mistress a huge iron key and surreptitiously crosses herself as the Count and his wife slowly walk toward the open double door.

"Personally," Adelaide says to her estranged husband as the doors close behind them and Marozia, the cook and maidservant, cocks her ear while pretending to adjust a trinity of gladiolas (today the wine merchants bring giant kegs of new wine from the hill towns to the neighborhood and even the wine merchant, a count from the Friulana region—he has heart trouble and stomps about angrily with a cane—even the wine merchant count climbs on the huge trailer and blows into the long rubber tube that conducts the wine from the barrels to other barrels in the catacomb twilight of the *cantina*, and his son, who has just bought a racy *white* speedster-roadster, jokes with the truckdriver and he too climbs up on the back of the truck where the *fiaschi* are piled like cargo on a sunken Phoenician merchant vessel, and he winks over at Leda, the pretty girl cashier of the bar across the street . . .) so as not to miss a word . . .

"Personally, I hope that they elect a foreign pope, or at least a pope who is not an Italian . . . because as long as we have an Italian pope we will not have a head of state to govern this Italian nation, but only a loud-talking little brother, afraid of the dark and the Light . . ."

The door closes and Marozia gazes up at the ceiling and again makes the sign of the cross . . .

"You should have written, or at least telephoned. It's not like you, Raffaele . . ."

"I didn't want to spoil your vacation. And besides, such an embarrassing humiliating operation—"

"Hemorrhoids . . . I suppose it *is* embarrassing for men. My father used to call it—"

"Please, Adelaide, I've been operated on, I've been humiliated sufficiently, shall we talk about something else?"

"The new Pope? Your prediction was right. Did I tell you that I saw Kennedy on my way to the airport? They stopped the bus near Ostia Antica for almost an hour. He looks something like you, really he does . . ."

"I suppose you mean that as a compliment, but *really*, Adelaide—"

"Is it the hemorrhoid operation or the nervousness of becoming a father that makes you so—so aggressive?"

"Do you mind if I have a drink?"

"I'll call Marozia—"

"No. Never mind. Frankly, I can't stand her any more. How can you stand her? She's neither a witch nor a nun. The way she lords it over you, you'd think she was—"

"A husband . . . Is that what you are trying to say?"

"I'll get the drink myself. That is if Marozia hasn't

deliberately changed the molecular arrangement of this house, now that she is so obviously in charge!"

"While I was in Greece, I thought a lot about us—for example, why we could never have a child. Whose fault was it, Raffaele? Yours or mine?"

"Adelaide—"

"No. Let me say what I want to say . . . The temples, the marble columns, Greece, all that mythology, the postcards. *Our* civilization, Raffaele—it didn't make sense to me. You and I, we loved each other—I think we still love each other. But you are about to become the father of an American Negro dancing girl's child. Those lizards racing over the dead white marble like motorboats! I hated Greece! Something is wrong! I am healthy. I ate like a horse in Greece. I went to Ephesus. The new Pope calls himself Paul. I wonder if he has ever been to Ephesus. What struck me most was the poverty. There were no trees. I became afraid of the sun. I hated that sinister purple sea. I felt like a tourist. I am sure the marble temples were a kind of joke. Built to fall. The trees. The silence. The humming of insects. All *that* was important and sacred. But not the white marble. What a terrible profession archaeology. Marozia was very rude with the guide, but I couldn't help laughing! Really I couldn't. Apparently someone the night before had had to relieve themselves. There were turds and a dirty newspaper I suppose whoever it was had used to wipe themselves with. It was an English newspaper. The *Observer*, I think. There was a photograph of that call girl on it—what's her name—Christine Keeler. Now isn't that funny. That German girl they found dead here in Rome —her name was Cristina too. Queen Christina of Sweden! Well, anyway. All I could think of was the headlines: KHRUSHCHEV ACCUSES CHINESE OF RACISM! Anyway, Marozia stepped in the mess, and you know what she said? . . ."

(It is 12:45 P.M., Friday, July 19, and I go out to buy the first edition of the evening papers, and I read in *Paese Sera:* "In the Early Hours of This Morning—EARTH-QUAKE IN NORTH ITALY—Great panic but no victim. The tremors felt in Val d'Aosta, in Piemonte, in Liguria, Lombardia and very strongly in Nice . . . Earthquake tremors struck North Italy provoking however only slight damage to things. Nevertheless, in some cities it was not possible to avoid scenes of panic with people fleeing their homes and seeking refuge in the streets of the suburbs. Professor Bini, assistant at the meteorological seismographical institute of Imperia, stated that, from registrations recorded by his institute, the earthquake tremors of 06:45 hours of this morning, were three, of which the first two were of an undulatory nature and the third—the most violent—of a sussultorial charac-ter . . .)

"Do you know what she said—?"

"Adelaide, stop laughing like that! *Stop laughing I say!*"

There is an urgent knock at the door. The door opens violently.

"Did the Count call?"

"No, the Count didn't call. And if you don't mind—"

"It's all right, Marozia! I was just laughing. *Dio mio!* I haven't laughed like this in years!"

"The melons weren't ripe after all, signora! They're hothouse melons!"

"Good for you, Marozia! Take them back to that mustached fool of a fruit vendor, and give his wife a piece of your mind! Tell her we've just come back from Greece where the melons and the figs were fresh! Not to mention the—"

"Adelaide! Stop being hysterical, I say!"

"Excuse me, darling. You can go, Marozia. Now what was I saying?"

(*La Stampa*, July 19, 1963: "MOSCOW REPLIES: WHO GIVES THE CHINESE THE RIGHT TO GAMBLE THE LIFE OF MILLIONS AND MILLIONS OF HUMAN BEINGS? Pravda comments: Peking does not recognize as revolutionary any action that does not smell of gunpowder!")

"Something about what Marozia said to the tourist guide in Greece—"

"Oh, it was scandalous, really it was—but so funny!"

"I'm sure it was—I didn't know Marozia could read English—"

"She can't. That's just the point—"

"Adelaide, will you please stop laughing and—"

"She said . . . she said . . . 'The English have to come all the way to Greece to do it out in the open and I have to come all the way from Italy to step in it!' "

"Very very funny, very funny indeed!"

"She said it in Italian, but everyone laughed! And it was *so* hot! The guide didn't laugh though. He offered her his handkerchief, and said something in French which even I couldn't understand. It sounded like '*Madame, voulez-vous danser avec moi?*' "

"Adelaide—!"

"And do you know what Marozia did with the handkerchief?"

"I think I'd better be getting back to the office—"

"She blew her nose on it. Loud. Like a shepherd's horn. Then she gave it back to him and said—"

"Never mind, never mind!"

"Oh, Raffaele, you *are* upset and nervous! Oh, and you've become so thin! It becomes you, though—"

"A few minutes ago you said I looked like Kennedy—"

"You do. I mean he looked, or at least reminded me of *you* . . ."

(*Il Giornale d'Italia*, Saturday, July 20, 1963: "FEAR FOR MARLON BRANDO. The actor at Santa Monica Hospital—MYSTERIOUS DISEASE—The doctors do not hide their preoccupations: the disease manifests itself rebel to their cures . . . Marlon Brando ignores the gravity of his condition and would like to recover soon to participate in the antiracist demonstrations . . . A Philippine actress initiates a court action against the famous actor: she affirms that she had had a daughter by him . . .")

"Reminded you of me? How?"

"Don't go . . . Stay . . . Stay, Raffaele . . ."

"Now you are crying, Adelaide. Why? It's not like you to be hysterical! Why are you crying?"

("The astronomists of the entire world are studying the enormous quantity of scientific material gathered during the total eclipse of the sun which on Saturday, July 20, interested Canada and the northern states of the U.S.A. This year for the first time the celestial phenomenon was observed from jet airplanes flying at a height of 12,000 meters at supersonic speed which permitted prolonging the duration of the observation and the photographing of the 'black sun' from an atmospheric stratum perfectly limpid." *Il Giornale d'Italia*, Monday, July 22, 1963. At 11:00 A.M. this morning, Claude Marchant, one of Katherine Dunham's dancers and a dancer-choreographer himself, telephoned to say that he has been in a tuberculosis hospital for many months and that he is looking for work. Acting on some strange impulse, a call, I have gone twice to the church Santa Maria della Pace, to see Raphael's painting "The Sibyls," perhaps to pray for peace: both times the church was closed.

Yesterday evening, Sunday, I went to S. Maria della Pace with my wife; the green twin doors were closed; I went to the open street door of the Teutonic College; the beefy doorman of the Teutonic College was confabulating with black-mustached men in a black automobile with a Genovese license plate, and said to me, 'We have nothing to do with that church Santa Maria della Pace, you must go ask the doorman of Number 5.' The doorman of Number 5 is a brilliantined-haired young man who is tortured by the idea that he deserves a better profession; the church, he says, is open only from 7:30 to 8:30 in the morning and more or less the same hours in the evening; since this day is Sunday— *Not the Sabbath: I think*—S. Maria della Pace is closed even at this evening hour, so I shall get up early tomorrow morning, first go to call upon Her Radio-active Majesty, Queen of Queens, Sister and Mother to Leonardo-Bramante-Raphael-Michelangelo, for the first time in my life I shall bow my head and pray to a madonna, then I shall return to my Piemonte-Mazzini-bureaucraticsaur quarter of Rome and buy my morning paper and read who shall have won the Liston-Patterson fight. My wife and I ate a pizza, *capricciosa*, near the Campo dei Fiori, and we looked at the lonely statue of Giordano Bruno: "What is a pizza, what is a heretic, is it not time now that cooks, *fabbro*, and pizza manufacturers *also* burn on the STEAK?"

"I'm not being hysterical, Raffaele . . . really I'm not . . . It's just that I'm amused . . . I mean . . . What I mean is, there is just nothing that can be done with life . . . The *Observer*, in Greece . . . English aesthetes without water closets when the moon is high, staring at temples . . . No trees . . . Poverty and figs and bread . . . What the guide said: '*Madame, voulez-vous danser avec moi?*' . . .

Oh, dear, my dear husband Raffaele . . . Isn't life interesting? Do you believe in God?"

"Kennedy . . . Do I believe in God? . . . Maybe there are no Negroes, just women and men . . . But is it necessary to *believe* in God?"

"When our husbands are away, we women shall play—theology and religion, we go to dressmakers and put on masks and take off masks and think of letters we should receive, and letters we should write . . . When our husbands are away, we women shall pray, we shall *play* with the idea of God! . . . '*Madame, voulez-vous danser avec moi?*' . . . That tourist guide in Greece, and *oh*, those lizards gliding over the marble, the heat, the explanations droned by drones of why ideas are born and die! . . . Sometimes I think the best ideas are the ideas that don't have to be dressed up in marble and stone! . . . Darling, forgive me . . . I can say these things, express these intellectual thoughts only because you are about to become a father . . . I am sad, so sad, Raffaele . . . No . . . don't touch my wrist . . . that used to be your little trick when we were engaged . . . Don't go to Greece . . . *Eros, eros, eros* . . . Have you ever played with the idea that perhaps *I* am the father of your child?"

(Doubts about the disease of Marlon Brando . . . It is insinuated that the actor feigned the disease so as not to speak to an anti-racist congress—Marlon denies all. *Momenta Sera*, Tuesday, July 24, 1963: LAS VEGAS: K.O. FULMINEO PER PATTERSON . . .)

"What if I were to make a film about our life, Raffaele?"

"Do you mean finance it?"

"No . . . *make it!*"

"Adelaide . . . I don't know what is happening to me . . . Women—you all make me confused! Has Maria Novella written you?"

"Oh, you do remember your sister—"

"I should have asked you this long ago. But what did she say about us when we were about to be married? I mean—she *was* your best friend in that . . . college . . ."

"She said . . . she said . . . you won't believe it . . . how time passes . . . she said . . . 'Be careful, Adelaide! Raffaele is in love with the *idea* of Africa . . .'"

"She knows I hate the idea of Africa . . ."

"We both keep saying the word 'idea' . . . there is no marble in Africa, in the *real* Africa, Raffaele . . . Perhaps that is why she was sent there as a nun . . . I mean . . . what I was saying about Greece . . . Green grass and bushes and weeds grow over marble, but the ideas live on . . . How many ideas there must be floating about in Africa . . . Gold and diamonds and uranium . . . But perhaps why they go there . . . They go for the ideas . . ."

"A film about our life! . . ."

"Since now I must sleep alone . . . I dream a great deal . . . My dreams are like films, Raffaele, like cinema . . . Oh, how I enjoy going to bed to dream about our life, our life in the present and the past, how our life could have been in the past future tense . . . Last night I dreamed of a name for your child . . . She shall be a girl . . . Her name shall be Annunziata . . . There shall be a parachute with advertising slogans on it . . . She shall land safely . . . And people shall applaud! . . . I am happy for you, Raffaele . . . Really, I am . . . I am happy for your American Negro dancing girl! . . .

"Well, Raffaele . . . Why don't you say something?"

"Excuse me . . . I was just thinking . . . What you said now about Africa. Of course you're right. Our father was intoxicated with the idea of Africa. Maria and I both suffered terribly. Those long absences. It killed our mother. And it was worse when he would come back from one of his explorations. It was worse because he was present in the house, but he was absent. He had a theory. He was going to write a book about it. But then he died . . . He said that Africa didn't exist *physically* . . . He said that Africa was a dream . . . That one day people on earth will dream of Europe, will dream of so-called white civilization, just like today they dream of Africa . . ."

"What a strange theory . . . and yet I think . . . I think perhaps he was very close to something true . . . Does your American Negro dancing girl *look* like an African?"

"Not really . . . I mean, she looks like a fashion model who happens to have dark skin . . . But sometimes—"

"I think I know what you are about to say . . . Sometimes she doesn't seem *real*, like embracing a girl in a dream . . ."

"How did you—?"

"In Maria Novella's last letter she said the same thing about the African children she teaches at the mission school . . . She said that sometimes when she is explaining something to them she has the feeling that she is in a dream, that her voice seems to fade away into silence and only her lips are moving . . . Then, she said, she makes them sing . . . She said that several times she thought she was going insane, but that when she told the missionary father—I forget his name—he said that he too had felt the same thing. But then he laughed and said it is only because they are so *humanistic* . . . I suppose she meant human, but in the letter she said *humanistic* . . ."

"I wrote her a letter just before Christmas, just before I knew about the child . . . I didn't finish the letter, I've been putting off telling her . . . Not because I'm ashamed of having this *meticcio* child . . . But because you and I have not had children. Adelaide, I love you . . . I love you . . . Why—?"

"I love you too, Raffaele . . . But you must give me time to think . . . Is it because I know that you are suffering . . . Is it because *I* feel superior (motherly superior) because you could not have a child with me, but are about to have one with an American Negro dancing girl . . . Is it because I pity you?"

"Adelaide . . . My dear sweet understanding Adelaide . . . I love you, I love you . . . I need you . . ."

"*Basta!* I don't think I shall make a film about our life after all! Marozia! You must go now, Raffaele! I must have time to think! I am your wife! I am not your mother! If I must dream of our life, past present . . . If *you* are the protagonist, if *you* must wear the blond wig, the shining boots, if you and your dauntless comrades must dash recklessly from one conquest to another, laughing and drinking, singing your love ballads under the moon and wiping the sticky blood from your exquisitely wrought swords, stay in the dream and be not a coward . . . I have no more milk for you, Raffaele, I am approaching middle life, I need time to think . . . Oh—! I've been brutal! Go now—think now of your Annunziata, your daughter. She, yes, needs milk! The milk of Raffaele della Porta, the same last name as the present mayor of Rome! You are a wolf, Raffaele, you have made a conquest! Your daughter— Oh, and if she or they are twins! Never mind, Marozia! The Count is leaving . . . They or she or he, the child, the children shall need milk. I . . . I . . . Oh, how my head aches! . . . I need time to think!"

IX

The Truce

A-TEST AGREEMENT IS "VICTORY FOR MANKIND," KEN-
NEDY SAYS . . . HE SEES WAR MORE REMOTE . . . KHRUSH-
CHEV HOPES FOR NEW THAW . . . NON-AGGRESSION PACT IS
STRESSED . . .

"QUAKE KILLS ABOUT 2,000, RAZES SKOPLJE, YUGO-
SLAVIA. Belgrade, July 26—An earthquake devastated
the slumbering Macedonian capital of Skoplje early

today, killing and injuring thousands and causing heavy property damage. The official Yugoslav news agency Tanjug quoted rescue teams in the shattered city, population 270,000, as reporting 'more than a thousand people have lost their lives' in the disaster . . ."

PEKING SAYS IT WILL HAVE BOMB SOON . . .

MARILYN MONROE EXCERPTS FROM 15 FILMS ON IN PARIS . . .

Today is Saturday, July 27, 1963, it is 6:00 P.M., for the first time in nearly a week here in Rome there are no magnetic storms, bus drivers drive carefully through the vacation-deserted streets, perspiration stains their gray shirts, they hold their breaths, elderly middle-class Romans sit quietly at sidewalk cafés, solemnly they dip their spoons into melting mounds of green and pink ice cream. Husbands with wives and children at seaside or mountain resorts roam the streets in their utilitarian automobiles, wearing loose sport shirts to hide their bulging waists, they try to pick up girls, but great is the demand, high the price; for the first time since the war the flow of speculative money here in Rome has dwindled down to a trickle. But the new poverty is genteel, is a kind of truce, a summer vacation in itself: waiters are grateful now for fifteen-lire tips, they are courteous, the wives of retired army officers are no longer ashamed of their prewar linen hats. Here in Rome, as solid silver spoons dip solemnly into melting mounds of green and pink ice cream, the news of the world is dramatic but irrelevant and remote . . .

But stretched out naked on her cotton cool sheets woven by *ergastolarum*, prisoners in for life on the prison island of Procida, Doris is thinking of the past future tense, is thinking of the child already stirring in her belly, the eternal future of the world, the past future tense of birth; Doris is thinking, is dreaming, but contained by the lead weight of gestative Time, Doris (without thinking, without playing praying, without *imagining*) slowly ritually solemnly strokes the belly hearth of *there where birth shall take place*, her long maternally gentle fingers designing the billion-old mysterious symbol of the spiral around the belly button mountainous height, Mount Ararat where Noah's Ark is *inhumed*, spirally Doris asks herself in dream memory or conscious thought: "The color of Adam and Eve, yellow, brown, black or white—?" And I too dream. Thief-like, a spiritual spy, I come. Doris, I shout (my lips move, there is no sound, nor does she see me, nor do I see myself, though I know I am *there*), Beginning and End are One, are Birth, have no color, have no face, Memory has turned to ritual and stone: Be not afraid, my Doris— the Spiral, that is your comfort, your secret, guard it wisely, eat well, guide the vulgar functions of your body, speak gently, hold your breath, guard that which must leave and that which must enter: the sacred twin doors . . .

(Today is August 1, 1963. My wife and son have just left for Procida on the 10:38 "sun train." My son will play with Michele of the Procida Scialoja tribe of patriots and jurists. My wife will work on a screen treatment of a new film entitled *Raffaello and La Fornarina*. Secretly, my wife is excited about this film. I am too. The director will be Gallone, the great though aging and youthful film director who has lived through the entire cycle of the "industry of dreams." I like him and have often conversed fruitfully with him. He made that first motion picture colossus, *Scipione L'Africano*. I like him because he was born in Luguria, province of flowers, and grew up in Naples, province of pessimism and song. Vesuvius, the Sixth Fleet, and domestic hanky-panky. *Carmine Gallone*, Rooster Red, shoe-shine boys and barbers, fraud and scandal, the miracle of blood, street singers: San Carlo Opera House! There I went with Gottfried von Einem for the première of his opera *Dantons Tod*, the derisive laughter of Neapolitan duchesses and dukes. And last night B.K. left. She is going to Greece. But is Greece truly the Mecca place of the mysteries hidden behind the street curtain of St. Maria della Pace? Now, as evening falls and the air stirs with quiet coolness, I return to the typewriter. I have been to the Schneider Gallery where Irene works. I again explained the strange esoteric meaning of the offering of the fish head on the clean white plate. This, yes, was a mystery, a mystery also to me! Cool and crisp, from Warsaw, she looked strangely like Laura: we (the Paris-Swiss educated sons of the gallery owner) talked of Padre Danilou, the price of paintings (I am practically penniless but by gallery standards some of the "works of art" I bought in a folly of love have gone up ten times in price: but time, always time, the judgment of—?). For example, Irene and the two Schneider sons—Alexander Schneider of the Budapest String Quartet who told me that I was about to become *riche* when my first novel was published, who, in Paris that long-ago year, in the most chi-chi inn, restaurant, gourmand's paradise, offered *me* the head of a fish (though the one I offered Irene was fried in heavy Roman grease, while Herr Alexander's—how well I remember now!—was *marinated*, the poem in my passport by Sandro Penna about sailors, an autograph, can it be sold even by *him?*)—Irene, whose beauty I recognize, whose mind I once—, and the two blond American Schneider sons, showed me a magnificent painting by Matta, painted in 1952, the year he and I went out on a marvelous party with Sophie and an Indian girl from Bombay, married to a steel magnate, but separated then from her Italian friend, he came back from a train trip, just when things were getting good!—Irene and the two Schneider sons said that the magnificent Matta was now priced at *ten thousand dollars!* How difficult and painful it is to be an artist!—too rich, too poor, too hot, too cold, *The Sorrows of Worthless Werther*, by Gertie, the manicurist's maid-in-waiting. For example: in B.K.'s second-*classe* compartment on the Crusaders' train to Brindisi, to Greece, there was a fake Ulysses, Italo-Americo-Greek, a fake sorrowing Werther, blond and blue-eyed with those gorilla-type black eyebrows that grow together in order to remind us that Sparta and Athens were always at war, this boy was short and stubby (he blinked behind his plastic eyeglasses and admitted that, *yes*, he was a mongrel, but *not* a Greek!), he spoke no *lingua franca*, he was enthusiastic about Greece, enthusiastic about the urine-odored second-class compartment, until a Hunter entered with a hunting hound called Cerebus that silenced even the old peasant women who hate both men and hate the sea and the land.)

That which must enter and that which must leave, the sacred twin doors . . .

Today is Monday, August 5, 1963, today's headlines: NUCLEAR TRUCE IN OPERATION TODAY . . . MANY FLOWERS FOR MARILYN MONROE . . . 13 USA SOLDIERS ATTACKED BY NORTH KOREAN PATROL . . . YOUNG WORKER DROWNS ON BEACH OF LADISPOLI . . . The Count takes off his jacket and hangs it on the doorknob of the bathroom door. There was no air conditioning in the tiny neighborhood branch bank where he had gone to cash a check for Doris. A woman had become hysterical about a *cambiale*, the final payment on a washing machine. "They can't do this to me!" she had screamed in the airless heat. "I am honest! Crucify me, you bloodsucking bankers want to crucify me! But I'll pay! I'll pay!" Just as the jolly fat cashier handed him the crisp stack of ten thousand-lire notes, an ambulance came to take her away. The Count does not look at

Doris' belly. He goes to the bathroom. He takes off his clothes. He takes a cold shower. It is cool and dark in the bathroom. As he dries himself his skin glows greenish-white like a plant in moonlight. Today is August 5th. A year ago we were on the beach of Ladispoli . . .

"A year ago today, we were on the beach of Ladispoli," he says to Doris as he stretches out alongside her on the cool cotton sheets woven by the *ergastolarum* in-for-life prisoners on the prison island of Procida. "Remember . . . ?"

THE SCANDAL WILL NOT FINISH WITH DR. WARD IN THE TOMB . . . IN LONDON MANY TREMBLE PERHAPS MORE THAN BEFORE OSTEOPATH'S DEATH . . .

"Marilyn Monroe had just committed suicide. We talked about the Russian astronauts. We talked about Adam and Eve. This year the Russians put a woman into space!"

"When you think about it, it's amazing how many things can happen in a year—"

"We talked about Adam and Eve, and now we shall have a child. If it's a boy we shall call him Adam, and—"

"—if it's a girl we shall call her Eve!"

The Count laughs, but he is not thinking about the child. He steals a glance at Doris' breasts. They are full and firm, seem already full of milk. He fights down an overwhelming impulse to kiss the stiffening nipples. He seems to hear Adelaide laughing. It is the porter's wife laughing with the baker's delivery boy down in the courtyard. No secrets in this thin-walled modernistic apartment house. "Serves him right, trusting all those bluebloods! Harems are fine for the hot-blooded darker races, but the English—they should stick to their horses and dogs!" The porter's wife laughs, blows her garlic breath on the jungle palms, the petals of flowers fall. The baker's delivery boy's footsteps are quick and nervous. An ambulance whines down the street. Accidents, the heat of a city in heat, and afraid, I wish Maria Novella were here . . .

Milk for the lamps of China—can milk burn, bring light to darkness?

"What did you say, darling? And, oh, look at you! You know I can't, not with me in *this* condition. What's happened to you, my sweet darling Count? You've become a regular stallion! My Lord! Why, you're magnificent! I want to give you a nice sugary kiss!"

La Sagra Della Bistecca

Today is Wednesday, August 14, 1963. I am in Cortona, in Tuscany, where M. has invited me to spend the Ferregosto holiday at his country estate. Quiet and restful, shady and cool, this park is paradise after the kaleidoscope scrambling of my vision that followed in the wake of my brother-in-law's tragic death. I remember: at ten o'clock in the morning, a phone call from my wife's uncle. Sergio has committed suicide, whiskey, sleeping pills, gas. The morning headlines that day: KENNEDY BABY DIES. Phone call to my wife, who is in Procida. My wife and son arrive. Sergio is dead. My son has a violent attack of diarrhea. Watery blood spurts from his anus. The first doctor wants to rush him to Regina Elena Hospital to operate for appendicitis. I object. The second doctor discovers that he is only suffering from liver trouble. He must go on a diet. The family must be united. Verano, the vast municipal cemetery of Rome. The father from Venice, the father-in-law, airplane pilot industrialist, friend of D'Annunzio. The two uncles, the hare and the tortoise. The cemetery workers in gray work overalls juggle the heavy pine wood casket. The "funeral" is chaotic, but, strangely, all are moved. In the cemetery, the city of death, the lawyers have shriveled. No one is more powerful than the low-paid cemetery workers now as they hoist the casket to a nice high niche in the unfinished edifice of reinforced concrete: this is my brother-in-law's monument. He admired Nervi, he built a staircase in Porto San Stefano which all said was impossible to build. My brother-in-law was a builder. As we drive out of the cemetery, pass other funerals entering self-consciously the city of the dead, I tell myself (tearless): "Whatever Sergio has built shall withstand the tempest, whatever Sergio has built shall long endure . . ."

But here at M.'s country estate it is quiet and restful, it is shady and cool. Here in this paradise park the silence is transparent, a harmonious weaving of myriad textured sound, not the opaque lifeless silence of the cemetery in Rome. My ear is constantly alert. I hear the breeze rustling leaves, I hear birds singing, I hear the aimless gossiping of chickens and turkeys and guinea fowl, the shrill melodious chirping of locusts. Flamboyantly bright like the banners of medieval pageantry the zinnias nod solemnly to one another against a backdrop of gray-green lawn and mournfully black-green cypresses. Last night shortly before dawn there came a sudden magnetic storm. Mario, the Count's butler, fell out of bed and woke up with a paralyzed left leg. Furiously, Annunziata, Mario's wife, strikes the blade of her scythe against the stone railing of the steps leading up to the door of her house. Sparks fly. Now, frowning darkly, she goes to the adjoining pasture to cut fodder for the animals . . .

(Today is Sunday, August 18, 1963, and Ben Johnson and I are on our way back to Rome. Fortunately we have taken an early train and we have the whole compartment to ourselves. A bull-necked sleepy-eyed man wearing the badges of mourning leaves the compartment in front of us and comes to sit in the empty compartment just across the aisle. He yawns, he licks his thick lips, he steals glances in our direction like a toad trying to outwit a fly. He opens his jacket and stretches out with his tiny fists on his hips. He is wearing a pistol holster. Ben and I exchange glances. Why is he so deliberately showing us this empty pistol holster? The man gets up and with just the barest hint of a smile on his full conceited lips he returns to his compartment and whispers something we do not hear to his younger companion, he too a bull-necked butcher type. "The Mafia!" Ben says under his breath. "Plainclothes policemen!" I counter hopefully, not at all convinced. The train speeds through a treeless invasion-scarred valley. Orvieto is near. Two flocks of tiny black birds glide over and under each other like rival squadrons adjusting their gunsights before an attack. I turn from the window. How pleasant it was in M.'s villa: there we were protected, we were inside a cool and shady placenta of seclusion and order, now we return to the unpredictable stormy lake which is Rome. I am vaguely uneasy. Ben is too. Almost simultaneously we light cigarettes. Ben lights mine, I light his. Ben's hand is trembling. I open yesterday's copy of *La Nazione:* "PRINCE PHILIP'S NAME IN WARD'S MEMOIRS . . . The husband of the Queen of England went to a party organized by the osteopath accompanied by a girl . . ." MORE CHINESE TROOPS ON BORDER OF INDIA . . . BUDDHIST PRIEST AND NUN SUICIDES MIDST FLAMES . . . MORE THAN FOUR THOUSAND BEEF-STEAKS CONSUMED DURING THE SAGRA DELLA BISTECCA AT CORTONA . . .)

Annunziata again crosses my line of vision carrying an armload of fodder. Christopher, a music student from Basel, comes out of the villa and sits down on the park bench opposite mine. We nod greetings. Then studiously he begins writing in his notebook. The afternoon

(*1 6* 7)

stretches and expands like a balloon being inflated. A black and scrawny turkey climbs a tree. Higher and higher. The turkey strains its neck, the turkey stands on tiptoes, the turkey wants to fly. A white baby turkey comes scurrying across the park and flies up on the bench beside me. I make the turkey sound in my throat, partly a guttural whistle, partly words: "Go-back! Go-back!" The turkey cocks its head and listens. It trembles all over. "Go-back! Go-back! Go-back!" The turkey becomes uncontrollably nervous. It makes a convulsive shiver and empties its bowels on the back of the park bench, a syrupy spinach-green liquid, then glides to the ground and trots back to join the guinea fowl. Last night a veterinarian came to kill the Count's bastard watchdog which, for no apparent reason, had begun to attack the guinea fowl, killing but not eating six of them. Surrounded now by these quietly lyrical grace notes of the Count's paradise park, I find it strange that people should become weary of life, should want to go to sleep and die. Laura, Marilyn Monroe, and now Sergio . . . Is there something about the age we are living in, does liver trouble create the smog of depression responsible for the weakening of the will to survive? We shall eat the turkeys and guinea hens, the dog shall be buried, the Count's villa is filled with photographs of mustached kings, grand dukes, princes and counts, Kaiser Wilhelm's triple-barreled horn, a book entitled *Il Diavolo* on the bookshelf next to *La Sacra Bibbia*, English bathtubs high and classily durable as Rolls-Royces, faded silk lamp shades, Persian rugs to mute our exuberant footsteps as we pass from one memory-cluttered room to the next, Ben Johnson, Christopher Schmidt, Pryce Zimmerman and I—we are always hungry, we wait for the tea-time bell to ring, the peach trees are small and slender, are overloaded with rose-fuzzed fruit, the flowers seem to dance, at night there is the feeling of dancing in the air, ghosts, invisible but benevolent presences stir rhythmically, sedately, I hear distant earthquakes, flowers open to the siren call of the invisible night singers, dogs howl in the distant Etruscan-haunted hills, unheard messages bombard the park from uncharted stars, I go to the well . . .

The well is enclosed in a cloister of ancient trees and flowering bushes. The well is permanently bonneted with a cement pyramid-shaped cover. The water can only be felt, in the humid August heat the water smells of corruption and death, the well has been sealed for over a hundred years, there is a plaque on the side of the well which reads:

DAWN WAS BREAKING ON THE MORNING OF JUNE 26 1861
AND
TWO YOUNG LOVERS
VIOLENTLY SOUGHT
IN THE WATERS OF THIS CISTERN
UNION IN DEATH
FILIPPO AND MARIA
GOD SHALL FORGIVE YOU
FOR GREAT WAS YOUR LOVE

The breeding of horses, the breeding of men, "good breeding"; M. takes us to visit Countess S. in her summer estate at Badia a Coltibuono in Chianti . . .

The Badia was formerly a monastery for the Benedictine monks. In the year 1812 the monks were expelled by Napoleon's troops. The Badia, or abbey, is haunted. Occasionally at night the monks can be heard singing in procession. After an hour and a half drive from Cortona, we climb the winding twisting road, sly servants show us into the cryptlike coolness, we wash up in the guest washroom, the mirror is set very low as though for a dwarf or a dog, three women are seated in the drawing room, the countess is tense, nervous, she is a widow, two of her sons have had violent deaths, the marchesa is studying a magical arrangement of playing cards, she smiles mysteriously, she is eighty years old and has a pleasant other-worldly odor and a lively imagination, she too is a widow, the third woman is a pink-dressed Florentine, calm and attractive, she was married to a handsome playboy Jew, she too is a widow, at once the tentacles of polite conversation begin probing the underwater remoteness of the place as in some long-drawn-out dream . . .

The old firm-fleshed marchesa talks on and on: Cardinal Rugambwa should have been elected pope—how *decoroso* he is!—the workers are better off than we aristocrats, they all have television and cars, I have several castles, one at Monte Jove, one at Basenello, you must come see my son's oven, he does ceramics, I have a son in the department of chemistry at the University of Rome, then one day during the war I found an English general in my bed, by mistake, you know . . . I know five languages, they all wanted me to interpret for them during the war, when you get back to Rome you must come have tea with me, I shall be back from my castle in Basenello in October . . .

At dinner, Ben and I sit on either side of the marchesa, conversation about traveling in airplanes, about Napoleon, the Benedictine monks were the first to plant the famous Chianti grapevines, the meal goes very very fast, neither Ben nor I have time to finish our glass of wine, coffee, then a visit to the park, a group of maple trees sent to the marchesa's son by Ezra Pound have failed to take root, are withering, talk of Berenson, there are plastic swans in the pool, one black, one white, visit to the wine cellars, visit to the chapel where there is a mysterious painting over the altar, full of symbolism (I remember a hand offering salt, a rooster . . .), executed by a monk from southern Italy, a mysterious relic removed from one of the walls: a bottle of olive oil and a parchment scroll, at 3:40 in the afternoon came violent explosions, a mine has been set off at the nearby quarry, the marchesa's chauffeur arrives, he has had an accident, his left foot is in a plaster cast, talk about Paula (Princess of Belgium), she has been oh so badly educated in Rome, she does not know yet what it means to be a princess, I write down the name and publisher of my first novel for the marchesa, who prefers mystery novels . . .

I am glad to leave, I am beginning to feel trapped inside a mystery novel myself, the nervous countess warns us about an unwatched railway crossing near Arezzo, I pluck a tiny yellow zinnia and put it in my lapel so as to ward off the spell of bad luck . . .

Today is August 15, 1963. It is the Day of the Assumption . . .

But now I am aboard this half-empty Pan American Jet crossing the distant leaden waters of the North Atlantic. It is August 27, 1963: I have made an important decision—I shall return to the United States, I shall try to find a job. "In all the years I've been flying, I've never encountered such powerful headwinds as these!" the elderly chief pilot whispers to the perfumed lady in the seat in front of mine. The winds are hurricane winds. The plane has almost run out of gas fighting them. The wispy cotton clouds are calm as a dream of lambs, but the passengers are beginning to sense imminent disaster. The pretty black-haired girl across the aisle straightens the hem of her stocking. All conversation has abruptly stopped. The metal shell of the plane shudders and whines as swiftly we descend for an emergency landing on Newfoundland . . .

Suddenly there is a river, a green and brown pattern of swampland. I am cold with fright, but studiously I pretend to be taking notes. I think of Leif Ericson, who has been here first, I think of my Viking friend, T. Then, suddenly, I begin to laugh. The tip of the silver wing feather touches the sluggish water of the river. The proud giant jet taxis to a stop. An Esso truck materializes out of the morning mist, the shiny bright red Esso letters are a Christmas-tree reminder that all is well in the world. But one glance at that primeval wilderness landscape awakens thoughts of dinosaurs, of overconfident civilizations sinking from sight beneath the slime and mud . . .

I am in New York! My oldest New York sister, Dorothy, is proud of her new apartment. There are huge picture windows offering a view of similar new apartment buildings and a glimpse of Central Park. Dorothy pours me a discreet drink of Napoleon brandy. The initial impression that I am in the observation tower of some utopian model prison soon gives way to a feeling of home and coziness. Dorothy bubbles over with plans. "You will stay in New York! You will get a job! America needs talent such as yours! You will get a very good job, you will never go back to Rome—you will stay in New York forever! But tomorrow, at the crack of dawn, you must board a Trailways bus, you must go to Washington, you must take part in the great Freedom March!"

The streets of Washington this 28th day of August, 1963, are strangely deserted, like the stylized set for a Civil War movie during the lunch hour recess. The driver turns down his radio and says over his shoulder: "They's pouring into the city at a rate of a thousand darkies an hour!" He laughs, and adds: "They closed the liquor stores for the duration of the March, but anybody wants any liquor only has to cross over the Maryland state line, ain't goin' to be any drunk darkies today. Now there might be some drunk white folks, how about that!"

My father laughs, but I can tell his thoughts are somewhere else. He profoundly enjoys historical events. By temperament he is one of those turn-of-the century foreign correspondents wearing a trenchcoat, covering some tedious Middle European war. I still remember that cold dreary day in Venice, seven or eight years ago, when he stood jauntily at the rail of the *traghetto*, like young Winston Churchill, snapping photographs of people and palaces along the Grand Canal, though there was no film in his brand-new Japanese camera . . .

"We are closed, but if your son has come all the way from Rome to take part in the Freedom March, then it certainly is our duty to accommodate him!"

The barber, a heavy agile elegant light-skinned man with slow-breathing measured gestures, turns up his transistor radio. Standing there heavily off balance, he listens to the news commentator chattering away about the March, then says, as woolly clusters of my hair fall to the floor like a sacrifice: "I don't know what these white folks is scared about—they might *call* this the Revolution of 1963, but you can bet your bottom dollar, ain't a single darkie out of the thousands and thousands pourin' into the city got anything that even halfway *looks* like a gun!" I am sleepy, it is hot and sticky, I think: "Yesterday I was in Rome . . ."

(Today is Friday, January 3, 1964. The new hopeful year has come at last. New Year's Eve, at midnight, I threw a pair of old shoes out the window, then blew two notes on my terra cotta flute in the general direction of the soaring full moon, then Emma, Tatina and I danced to music pouring out of the television set. Emma's forehead was as warm and soft as a young girl's. Tomorrow Pope Paul goes to the Holy Land. Says this morning's *Il Messaggero:* EXALTATION IN THE HOLY LAND . . . CHRISTIANS AND MOSLEMS WAIT WITH EQUAL TREPIDATION THE VISIT OF THE AUGUST "PILGRIM" . . . PRESS CONFERENCE OF KING HUSSEIN—PERHAPS ON MOUNT ZION THE MEETING BETWEEN THE POPE AND THE HEAD RABBI NISSIM . . . Pontius Pilate or Saint Francis? The Holy Land is an ugly vineyard devastated by clean desert winds and petty family quarrels over property and wills. Will the Pope "wash" his hands in dirt? Suddenly now as I remember the shortest verse in the Bible, "Jesus wept . . .", the legs of the thronelike barber chair I am sitting on give away and I tumble to the floor. From the next room comes my wife's voice: "What has happened? Did you fall?")

(Today is Saturday, January 4, 1964. Today for me is

a strange and powerfully happy day. The sun shines with diamond brightness on Rome, but a clean cold wind torments the palm trees across the street. I awakened early. I turned on the TV set. While Emma and Tatina, who was still angry with me for staying out until two o'clock in the morning, studiously, rebelliously, did House Work, I watched the Pope leave for the Holy Land. People had begun calling him Paolo Mesto (Sad Paul), but now he does not look so sad. As I write, his plane speeds swiftly toward the land where Christ was born. Paul was a tiny figure in the circular porthole, a lonely pilgrim, a tourist. For some reason I am profoundly moved by this pilgrimage. Just as I am profoundly annoyed that no one else in the house—or so it seems—shares my emotion. New Year's Eve Alex again declared himself an atheist. Last night hours and hours of idle talk with V. and another young Sicilian about the Mafia and political assassination. Does Antonio believe in God? He offered me three kinds of olives—gray, green and black—from Sicily. The fierce pride of Sicilians for their land makes me jealous. What do Sicilians think of me? Do they consider me a Moor? In the terra cotta plate of gun-metal black olives there was one small segment of a garlic. God and the Devil. We talked of Christ, and I said that He was a big man and left big hand- and footprints. Then I repeated the thought I had yesterday: I said that I hoped Pope Paul would, to repair the historical damage of Pontius Pilate washing his hands in water, wash his hands in oil. Oil, even the oil of the

Middle East, can now be, miraculously, turned into food. Oil derives from, among other things, the bodies of fish, sardines, the miracle of Jesus Christ! Lord of Light and Reason, I am grateful now for the schizophrenic jigsaw puzzle which slowly now begins to reveal a Face . . .

Today even the Roman cynics are uneasy without their Pope . . .)

(Today is Sunday, January 5, 1964. This morning's headline in *Il Messaggero* proclaims: THE PONTIFF HAS PRAYED ON THE SEPULCHER OF CHRIST . . . THE POPE ALONE MIDST A WILDLY CHEERING CROWD AS HE WALKS DOWN THE VIA CRUCIS . . .)

Never in my life have I seen so many Negroes in one place. This Freedom March is a continuous flow of smiling dark faces. Slowly the clean well-groomed self-conscious well-behaved crowd of marchers shuffles past the solemn neoclassic government buildings. In the distance under the clear blue sky the Lincoln Memorial can barely be seen. There is sporadic singing: "We shall overcome someday . . ."

I think: "Yesterday I was in Rome. As yet I do not feel part of this well-groomed well-behaved revolution. To the contrary, I feel somehow cheated. It all seems like some gigantic hoax, a public relations stunt. Everything seems false, contrived—the mobile drinking fountains and latrines provided by the Army, the sleek blue-and-white or red or green aluminum buses parked in orderly rows, the blue-uniformed drivers standing in quiet groups like undertakers, chewing gum, in their roles of logistic agents, remote from both life and death; photographers and TV cameramen perching on hastily erected platforms of iron tubing, "historifying" the Event; the Red Cross tents, a Pepsi-Cola mobile unit dispensing drinks and sandwiches, the government buildings closed for business, but ghostly faces peering down at the marching Negroes from upper windows. No one throws candy wrappers on the carpetlike government lawns; I scatter the tobacco of my cigarette butt and roll up the paper into a tiny tiny ball, as I was taught to do in the Army . . ."

And my father says nothing. He is meditating—like a cattle merchant—on his pipe, but the pipe is not lit. We have no tape recorder. *His* father sold baked sweet potatoes from a pushcart on the slum streets of Philadelphia. *My* son is a Roman schoolboy watching this Freedom March on tomorrow's TV in Rome. And here we are, father and son *in the presence, in the present*, marching. Where? It does not matter. The Freedom March is people. Thousands and thousands of shuffling feet, polishing the paving stones of history and time. There are pretty girls, Negro and white, there are too many ugly girls, untransformed, there are priests and preachers and ministers and missionary types with scrawny self-righteous necks, there are members of Catholic fraternal groups carrying vulgar madonna banners, there are militant Jewish ladies from the garment industry unions of

New York. "There ain't been nothing like this in Washington before!" a disembodied voice behind me says. And suddenly it doesn't seem real, there are too many people, I haven't the slightest idea what we are doing here, where we are going. *To a tomb?* For a while longer I let myself be swept along with the flow of the mournfully singing crowd. Now I am hungry. We hail a taxi. My mother greets us at the door. She puckers up her lips so that I may bend down and kiss her. As a child, it always embarrassed me to kiss my mother, but now I do so almost eagerly, as an anchor to fix my position in time and space. "Welcome home, big boy!" my mother says.

(EXTRAORDINARY TIMES. *Il Giornale d'Italia*, January 11, 1964: "How many extraordinary events in the passage of a few weeks! In Italy, in Europe, in the whole world great winds of change are blowing. It is useless to close our window to these winds of change; we cannot isolate ourselves, we cannot withdraw into ourselves. The dramatic death of Kennedy, the socialists participating in the government with the Catholics, the "pilgrimage" of the Pope to the Holy Land, the journey of Chou En-lai to many countries of Africa, American grain being shipped and sold to the Soviet Union, the recent attitudes of Paris toward the nations of the Afro-Asian bloc and, in particular, toward China, and, today, the exceptional visit of Paul VI to the President of Italy, Segni . . .")

(And on an inside page of the same edition:

"YESTERDAY ON THE COAST OF CALABRIA . . . REPEATED THE PHENOMENON OF 'MYSTERIOUS LIGHTS' IN THE WATERS OF SANT' EUFEMIA MARINA . . . OUR CORRESPONDENT WITNESSED ALONG WITH OTHER PERSONS THE APPARITION OF THE LUMINOUS 'DOLPHINS.' Nicastro, January 11—Two evenings ago, in the waters of Sant' Eufemia Marina, a strange phenomenon took place; to verify the foundation of the news we visited a trattoria ten kilometers from Nicastro, situated on state highway 18, along the Tyrrhenian coast, a hundred meters or so from the beach. Inasmuch as the phenomenon had been seen from that locality and the proprietor of the trattoria, Carmine Crialesi, his wife Carmela La Chinia, his sons Carlo, Pasquale, Palmerino and Giuseppe, as well as his relatives Innocenza La Chinia and Ettore Iera, have sworn to the veracity of what took place, we were anxious—so as to have precise information—to briefly interview the above-mentioned eyewitnesses.

"All were in agreement in declaring: 'It was about ten P.M. and we were serving the last customers of the evening when through the windows of the balcony, we could see on the sea, about three hundred meters from shore, about twenty luminous objects, all the same size, proceeding slowly in the direction of Capo Suvero. Curious to know just what the strange objects were, Carmine, Pasquale, Palmerino and Iera approached those luminous bodies aboard their fishing launch *Santa Maria* until they were able to pull up close to one of the objects, which was about three meters in length. The object was covered all over with spines, and on its back, each separate from the other, were strange protuberances, of various heights, conical in form. It was not possible to establish if they were habitants of the sea or metallic bodies. The waiter Iera touched the marine "monster" with one of the oars but at contact with the scaly body the oar seemed to become iron and the youth had the sensation of having received a violent electrical shock. At this point, so as not to take unnecessary risks, we hastened back to shore while the strange beings vanished on the horizon, emitting sinister intermittent beams of light . . .' ")

Doris has changed, and frequently seems to purposely become a part of the machine she is driving, the idling motor as we wait for the traffic light to change seems to have become the beating of her heart. The change that has come over Doris, her voluntary withdrawal from me and the novel I am writing about her, this new passion of hers for automobiles and driving (she claims that only while driving does she find peace and relaxation, that moving in automobile traffic provides her with a feeling of purpose, of being like other people, while sitting in her new apartment, waiting for the telephone to ring, or watching the TV set, gives her the feeling of aging, makes her skin itch, reminds her that she has no home), both fascinates and repels me, I have the feeling I have had before that it is she who is vampirizing me, that it is she who is writing this book . . .

So I say, while watching a young girl at the wheel of a Fiat 500 that has just pulled up alongside Doris' Lancia pull an untidy checkbook out of her purse, put on a pair of black horn-rimmed glasses, and hastily, nervously, write out a check: "I told you my wife and son and I spent Christmas in Siena at the villa of my wife's uncle, who is a well-known lawyer there. Well, the day we arrived, hired peasants were cutting down a stately walnut tree, because the tree was no longer producing fruit in commercially profitable quantity. The Tuscan peasants with their long axes had dug a pit so as to better hack away at the roots. They grinned up at me like satyrs and spit on their hands. Chips from the roots began to fly, and a feeling of great sadness came over me for the loss of the tree. The next day fog drifted over Siena, and I could not see the bell tower in Piazza del Campo. I wandered through the twisting streets, through the fog. I went to the Cathedral. The marble decorations on the floor were softly worn. I got lost in the fog. I was almost outside the city limits when I came to a hospital, to the Botanical Gardens. Then I found a narrow straight street with high walls on either side, called Vicolo della Fontanella. This street led me back into the city. I went into a small church with a Roman-esque façade where there was a *presepio* and an exhibition of the Bible. Then I went to my wife's uncle's law office. There were shelf after shelf of books of law. The date of the earliest book of Italian law was 1874. He drove me through the fog back to the villa in his Citroën.

When my wife and I returned to Rome, several days later, we wrote a letter to thank her uncle and aunt for their hospitality. My wife asked me to include a message to our son, James, who had remained behind, and I said, 'There is no axe in all the world capable of wounding a walnut tree that has been cut down . . .' When my son returned to Rome, he told me that when the walnut tree fell down, it severed an electric wire, that the electric wire dropped down on a puddle of water, that a sow belonging to the peasants who had cut down the tree crossed the puddle and was electrocuted . . . Have the initiates become lay?"

At last the light changes. With a slight jerk the car leaps forward. I have the feeling that Doris has not been listening to me, that I have been talking to myself . . .

Doris' new apartment is on Via Giulia, not far from where Laura lived, a few minutes' walk from Alice's apartment. I have never liked this street, though architecturally it is one of the most stately in Rome. Somehow it evokes in my mind all that was cruel and futilely pompous in papal Rome. There is a feeling of intrigue and poisonous plotting of servants, criminal collusion between moneyless aristocrats and a falsely good-humored proletariat that respects neither dogs nor cats. On Via

Giulia is located the Criminal Museum where elaborate instruments of torture are placed on display. One has the feeling that dark pre-Christian cults of death and sexual perversion still thrive in the dungeon dampness of those fortresslike palazzi of austere classical design. For some strange reason, foreigners find it "romantic" to live in the cramped servants' quarters of these fetid crime-haunted buildings. The market people wait for news of the latest suicide, the bearded Englishman gone berserk. Via Giulia is Rome at its cynical worse. And yet Doris says that she is happy here, that the neighborhood people are "real" and "human," that unlike the fascistic middle-class and modernistic quarter of Parioli, people here are interested in her and call her by name . . .

"You left so suddenly," Doris says as we enter the warm dark hallway.

"I went by Pan American. As you remember, I went to the U.S. to look for a Job. There were hurricane winds over the North Atlantic. The plane ran out of gas. We had to land in Newfoundland to refuel. I came back by ship. On the *Saturnia*. The return journey took thirteen days. We docked at Naples, December twentieth. From Naples I took my favorite luxury train. A big German sat next to me in the dining car and kept trying to elbow me out of my seat . . .

"I felt so alone. The next day I got a letter from my mother telling me that she had just married an undertaker. She and her husband, my stepfather, were on their honeymoon in the Virgin Islands. She said that if what I was looking for in Italy was the sea and the sun then I should come to the Caribbean, I should come to the Virgin Islands. She said it was more patriotic to patronize one's own sea and sun . . .

"The day before the *Saturnia* docked at Lisbon, the boatswain told me that the night before, a ballet chorus of dolphins had danced around the ship. This was a sign of good luck, he said. Also cockroaches came out of their hiding places behind the walls of the bar. The Spanish journalist, one of my table companions, nervously killed one of the cockroaches. But William L., the mysterious cook who had worked for a family of Park Avenue millionaires for over thirty years and who was now going home to his native Barcelona to retire, he didn't kill any of the cockroaches. I didn't know that cockroaches traveled on ships . . ."

"I suppose you want to know about the baby . . . A baby is birth, so I suppose you have come to see the baby. I guess it is natural for people to be curious about birth. But when those other people from that other place use a woman's body for the taking place, the happening, of Birth . . . the woman becomes old. If not in body, in mind. William, William, I do not feel generous. I *do* resent being used as a subject for your novel. I *do* resent being used as an island-place where Birth takes place. And yet I suppose someone has to be the woman where Birth takes place . . . Do you feel more guilty as a writer or as a man? But something has happened to you in America, since the last time I saw you. You are thinking about something else, you are not thinking any more about guilt . . . You're not thinking about your novel, you're not thinking about me . . ."

("*Paese Sera.* Tuesday, January 21, 1964: FIERCE CRIME IN VIA LAZIO . . . VICINITY OF VIA VENETO . . . EGYPTIAN ASSASSINATED WITH FOUR PISTOL SHOTS—The victim is the *commerciante* Faruk Chourbagi (age 27) . . . He was probably killed Saturday evening, in the office of Tricotex: the assassin threw acid in his face and then fired four shots at him face to face . . . The palazzo of the crime is only a few meters from the building where Christine Wanninger was slain . . .")

("Does man possess a rational will or only a complex set of responses to stimuli? Agamemnon, Clytemnestra and Aegisthus all act under compulsions but rationalize their deeds as just. There are close ties between Aeschylus and modern Freudian literature, for each assumes some deep, consistent patterns beneath our tangled deeds and feelings.

"Sin or crime has a chain reaction in Aeschylus. Evil begets evil with almost the same inevitability as Newton's Third Law of Motion, that 'for every action there is an equal and opposite reaction.' Aeschylus was concerned with how the chain of evil could be ended, but it is not surprising that he saw it as a sort of divine or 'natural' law in operation . . . Evils purge evils, but when will the chain of evils end?")

"You still haven't asked about the baby . . . You know what I have learned from all this? This funny experience of ours—I mean since you started writing a novel about me? You know, William, what I have learned? That having a baby makes the mother be born! Don't laugh. Wait, I'll get you a drink ... Here ... Is that enough ice? ... What I was trying to say is that the baby gets born later, maybe when it's thirty or forty years old, even! But the mother gets born right away. Right away. As soon as the lights come on, and she opens her eyes, and she sees it moving and trying to wink and crying and dripping wet, all red and alive and already wrinkled like an old man or an old crone, just like it has just come out of a washing machine. And you take a funny deep breath, and you're kind of ashamed, because, after all, what did you really do, but let yourself be used. But really, William—isn't it funny I'm calling you William now instead of Bill?—but really, I tell you, just that moment when the lights come on and you see it, the baby I mean, well that's when you get born, you're torn loose from some fuzzy kind of roots, and you're alone again, you can fly, that's what I mean about being born, but the baby, if it's a man, won't have that feeling until much much later, that is if he is lucky, but a girl baby, a girl baby will have that funny being-born feeling, that feeling of being alone and capable of flight, that flying being-born feeling, the moment the lights come on and you can see it, the baby I mean ... I guess you think I'm crazy raving about having a baby like this?"

(But there is no baby. Doris knows there is no baby. *I* know there is no baby. Doris, Doris, why do you lie?)

(*1 8 7*)

"The bed in which Abraham Lincoln died is as small as a torture rack in the Criminal Museum in Rome. That next day after I almost got into a fight with the young Irish grocery store delivery boy, I had lunch at the San Marino restaurant with a friend of a friend. A gallant editor, a man whose wife had recently died. He was nervous and I was nervous. There was a colorful gouache in his Fifth Avenue office by Bemelmans. For a moment it cheered me up, for I was seeking a job; it reminded me of another good-eating Europe than the snarling gray Europe I had left. The San Marino restaurant is a good restaurant. The last time I was there, several years before, to do research on a movie to be called *Little Italy*, there was a pretty blond hat-check girl from somewhere around Sant' Arcangelo di Romagna, or maybe she was from Bologna. Anyway she was opulently Bolognese, a very warmly appetizing girl. Just to look at her made me hungry. But that morning, or rather, that lunch hour there in the San Marino, neither of us was hungry. I ordered something delicious with mushrooms and crabmeat. The editor friend of a friend is like a cavalry officer from Texas. I told him my training had been in the cavalry in Texas with the Ninth Cavalry Division. I wore spurred boots and a cavalry hat on my first furlough back to Clarksburg, West Virginia, where my father's company, the Hope Natural Gas Company, affiliate of the Standard Oil Company of New Jersey, had transferred our family from Pittsburgh, where we were born and had grown up, in the mysterious banker Von Bonheur's experimental village of Fairywood, where the great jazz saxophonist Bob Cooper, his brother, and my brother, gave jazz concerts in our shanty built in a tree, this was in 1937 when Hitler was blitzkrieging, and Benny Goodman was our god, when there were no jazz concerts except those we gave from our perch in the shanty on the top of the tree in Fairywood, we talked about why we were nervous, the editor friend of a friend and I, we were nervous about gangsters and financiers and cybernetics and slavery and the generous Aga Khan, about Harvard, about the underground tremor of violence that was threatening the neoclassic structure of Jeffersonian America, remembering the days in that hot dusty Fort Clark on the Mexican border when I was training in Texas for the game of war, the trucks that would transport us across the border to Villa Cuauhtémoc to the concentration-camptype whore houses, with little fourteen-year-old girls, their mothers and fathers, waiting to receive us Yankee military men, remembering most vividly of all the concentration-camp-type prophylactic stations on the American side of the border, the hundreds and hundreds of Negro cavalrymen crouching over the zinc stands, squirting derivatives of *permanganate potassico* in and about their genital organs under a bright Texas moon, I dabbed listlessly at my mushrooms, my editor friend did likewise, he asked the waiter if he could have another drink, the waiter, a distinguished gentleman with secret authority, with knowledge gained in the medieval in-

(1 8 9)

trigues of pre-Renaissance Lombardy, said yes—then, only then, did my editor friend confess that he was alarmed, that he was concerned, the future of the country is in danger, there are sinister forces, I told him about my fight in the bar, but, I said, we must not be dismayed, the country will rise to the crisis, I did not, could not have known, that two days later President Kennedy would be assassinated, I said, dabbing listlessly at my mushrooms, *the adrenalin of the country is rising*, there is violence in the air, my editor friend spoke of how the dog in his house became listless and unhungry when his wife was about to die, America is a great and courageous country, I said, we shall survive, the hat-check girl helped me into my coat.

"No. I don't think you're crazy. The world's maybe crazy. No one wants birth any more. Everybody's afraid of the Event . . . *advent*. Everybody's afraid of what the *third* thing might turn out to be . . . Did you know that Valentina, the Russian girl who flew in a space ship—did you know she is pregnant? She will call on the Queen."

(*Paese Sera*, Friday, January 24, 1964: "IN THE PROVINCE OF KWILU . . . THREE MISSIONARIES KILLED IN THE CONGO—The Catholic mission at Mukedi burned: seven nuns saved . . .")

"I wanted to name the baby John, you know, because of Pope John, and John Kennedy, for what they both did. Giving birth to whatever it was you mean by the '*third* thing,' using the manly weapon of dialogue, instead of the old womanly weapon of poison and the bargain-basement gun. But the Count, when I told him I wanted to name the baby John, he made some sarcastic comment in French, then he got angry, he had been drinking a lot, I think he is having terrible trouble with his wife, whom I have never met, and he said 'Why don't you name the little bastard Fu Manchu, why don't you name him 'Monsieur Nhu'?'"

(*"Vitriol.* late ME.L. *vitriolum.* f.L. *vitrum* glass. One or another of various native or artificial sulphates of metals used in the arts or medicinally, esp. sulphate of iron . . .")

(*Paese Sera*, Friday, January 24, 1964: "THE VITRIOL FOR THE LAW IS AN AGGRAVATING CIRCUMSTANCE—The vitriol has returned to public attention. Used, particularly, with the mentality typical of the vendetta, to symbolize, perhaps, the absolute contempt for the person to be punished, it seems, especially with those populations and individuals who have been formed through time with a kind of atavistic predetermination and resignation to facts well-defined and delimited, especially in the professional field . . . The vitriol has returned to public attention five days ago, when the ferocious—it has been noted that it is mainly women who use this extremely dangerous substance—murderer, after having repeatedly shot the Egyptian industrialist Faruk Chourbagi in the face, threw, as a gesture of supreme contempt, a jet of the corrosive acid at the face of the young man, to disfigure it . . .")

"Kaiser Wilhelm, the 'Iron Duke.' What a problem it is to give names to babies! Why did my mother call me William—or sometimes in the afternoon, since she was raised in Pennsylvania, among the Pennsylvania Dutch, she would call me *Wilhelm!* Now my wife's relatives call me Zio Bill, but perhaps they would prefer to call me Uncle Tom? I don't know. Truly, this is the first time I have ever thought about the names people are given. It is also the first time I have wondered about the mysteries of alchemy!"

("AD AGENCY INDICTED FOR 'SELLING' PILL. New York, Jan. 23, 1964 (AP)—A Manhattan advertising agency was indicted today on Federal charges of fraudulently promoting a worthless weight-reducing pill in a multi-million-dollar television newspaper and magazine campaign . . .")

("PARIS ENVOY TO PEKING—As the establishment of Franco-Chinese diplomatic relations becomes increasingly imminent, two leading candidates for the job of French Ambassador in Peking have emerged . . .")

("THE ARIZONA MAFIA—It is only natural for Barry Goldwater to seek out trusted friends from back home to be at his side for the greatest undertaking of his life . . .")

("ATROCITIES—It is horrible to read about all those German atrocities against humanity in World War II. But if you people cannot forget that which happened 23 years ago, how can you then forget the two million innocent souls of children, women and old men killed by the French in Algeria a few years ago? I think we Arabs should deal with the responsible French militarists—and there are some very special ones among them to bring to justice—even if we have to take the matter into our own hands, the same way the Israelis are doing with these Nazi beasts . . .")

(CASSIUS CLAY ADDRESSES BLACK MUSLIMS, MAY BE MEMBER OF ANTI-WHITE SECT . . .)

"It was incredible, Doris, the high pitch of hatred and violence I felt in New York—in America—as soon as I got back from Washington. It was if some satanic super-sonic whistle were being blown, one of those high-frequency whistles they use to call dogs with, but one so big it was driving people to the point of madness all over the United States. The TV stations broadcast two-hour specials about the Freedom March, and hatred against Negroes grew. I went to a Black Muslim meeting in Harlem to hear Malcolm X speak, and he raved and ranted against white people, and against the Uncle Toms who had let themselves be sucked into participating in the Freedom March. He urged the crowd to buy Black Muslim bean pies, and warned the black women present that if integration of the races took place, the white women were already mobilized to steal all their black men from them . . . Two big husky black women in the crowd standing next to me began shrieking, 'Blood! We want blood! Kill the cops! Kill the cops!' They thirsted for blood.

"Then, on a Sunday afternoon, my sister phoned me from Alabama to tell me that someone had thrown a bomb in a Negro church in Birmingham, killing five young girls who were attending a Sunday school class . . .

"And the supersonic dog whistle inciting the nation to violence blew stronger and stronger. Two days before President Kennedy was assassinated, I almost got into a fight with a young Irish boy in an Italian bar.

"The young Irish boy, he worked in a grocery store as a delivery boy, he asked me if I was a cop. He said that if I was a cop the 'Mob' would handle me. I was scared—I'll never forget that night. On the side wall of the bar there was a framed picture of President Kennedy next to a framed picture of a race horse. The owner of the bar, or the barman, kept an old-fashioned billy club in the drawer of the cash register. I asked him to let me see it. It was heavy, loaded with lead. The young Irish boy became more and more belligerent. A Negro intellectual from Boston who lived in the nearby middle-income housing project hid his face in his arms and moaned: 'Oh no, no, *no* . . . this is *just too much!*' The supersonic dog whistle of violence screamed louder in my ear. I went up to the young Irish boy, I grabbed his arm. 'No, I'm not a cop,' I said. 'I'm a writer.' Why did he threaten me with the 'Mob'?"

(Today, Saturday, January 25, Emma and my wife bought a set of stolen silverware for which they paid the sum of thirty-five thousand lire. Emma said that the purchase was a bargain. My wife said that the man who

knocked at our door while we were taking our afternoon nap, during which we made warm and ardent love,
we are husband and wife, was Neapolitan and that he put
on a very good show . . .)

"The Count's sister, the nun from the Congo, her
name is Maria Novella, came to visit me. She was flying
back to Leopoldville the next day. She stayed all afternoon and we had a long talk. Mostly we talked about the
Count. She said their father was a fanatic about Africa.
He was always going off to Africa, to hunt or to explore
or to fight wars. When he would come home, all he
would talk about was Africa. The Count grew up hating
everything that had to do with Africa. He would become almost neurotic any time the subject of Africa was
brought up. He would say, even when he was a boy,
'Who wants to be reminded of that stinking green jungle
mess where the whole human race comes from?' The
Count hated his father and he hated Africa. This made
the Count's sister feel guilty, so she became a nun and
asked to be sent to the Congo. As simple as that. She
became a nun the same year her father died from some
intestinal infection he caught in Africa. She said she's not
afraid of Africa. She said the problem with Africa is that
they speak there a *human* language the rest of humanity
has almost forgotten. Africa is not wild, she said, it's just
a *real* place, the people there haven't learned to think or
talk like a machine yet, in Africa, she said, people think
and talk more like an IBM electronic brain than like a
combustion engine. I guess what she means about Africa

and the Africans is that Africa and the Africans are kind of 'offbeat.' But if I understood her right, in her opinion the new world that is slowly taking shape now, the way society will have to become to survive and not go under, be sucked back down into the mud, will be like Africa and the Africans, will have to be 'offbeat,' will have to forget the squarish cadence of the steam engine and face the electronic and mathematical, the *red and the green* realities of the tom-tom bed, the subtle cluckings of the Bantu tongue. Then she said something in Latin, what she said I don't know, I could not understand, but what she said sounded beautiful, and I could tell that Latin, the way she spoke it, was not a square language, many of the sounds and rhythms of what she said to me in Latin were female, while others were line-straight and stood up stiffly like soldiers holding spears. What was it the Count's sister said to me in Latin? Maria Novella in the Congo! Daniel in the lion's den! . . ."

("IT'S MANELESS. The Jungle Dress, by H. B., Paris, Feb. 3—The jungle is in mourning. First the leopard, then the panther, then the jaguar, the monkey, the tiger. Now it's the lion's turn to be trapped and made into a dress by Chombert . . .)

(*New York Herald Tribune*, Paris, Tuesday, February 4, 1964: "STATUS SYMBOL OF LARGE FAMILY DEPLORED IN U.S. Washington, Feb. 3, 1964 (UPI)— Americans must give up the 'status symbol' of large families because the U.S. population is growing at a crisis pace, a population expert said today. Robert C. Cook, editor of the nongovernmental Population Reference Bureau's 'Population Bulletin,' said that if present trends continue the U.S. population will rise to 249 million by 2000, and to one billion in 2065. Mr. Cook said that at present the average number of children born per woman in the United States is three. A reduction of this rate to 2.5 'would beneficially alter the state of things to come for Americans in the year 2000 and beyond.' In order to accomplish it, Americans must recognize the fallacy of their cherished philosophy that there is always room for one more. Today, like many of our other status symbols, large families represent unrealistic goals and values . . .")

(SAIGON GIRLS "TWISTING" TOO MUCH)

(DUTCH BOY SCOUTS "ADOPT" MASAI TRIBE)

(RED SPACEWOMAN, VALENTINA, TO SEE QUEEN ELIZABETH)

("*Think not: How Big America! Think: How Young America!* . . . Focus a camera anywhere in the United States and the picture is the same—young Americans dominate the scene. Young people are fast becoming the citizen and consumer majority. Within this decade, 55% of the U.S. population will be under 30. Young women now number an unprecedented 21,000,000! A new consumer generation, they're creating America's new mores and modes. Young women are influencing everything from finance to fashion . . .")

("CLEVELAND MOB BEATS TWO NEGROES. Cleveland,

Jan. 30, 1964—A wild crowd of several hundred persons beat two Negroes, shoved photographers, and threw bottles, fruit and eggs, during a school integration dispute today. Police cordons kept the crowd back from the predominantly white Murray Hill School to which Negro pupils from overcrowded schools were being transferred by the school board. The demonstrators apparently were unaware that the United Freedom Movement and the Hazelsell Parents Association had agreed in a predawn meeting to call off scheduled picketing and meet with school board members and civic leaders to review the situation. Eggs, grapefruit and bottles were thrown at a priest and a Negro clergyman, who attempted to quiet the crowd. Police said two Negroes were beaten by the crowd. The two men said they went to the school to protect their children. Four photographers, two Negro and two white, were beaten and their equipment smashed when they tried to approach the school from the rear. Police rescued them. About 35 uniformed policemen, plus plainclothes men, were at the scene. From the steps of the school a Catholic priest told the crowd the Negro pupils would leave as soon as police could escort them out of the place. 'Jesus Christ wasn't black!' some in the crowd yelled. 'God wasn't black!' *New York Herald Tribune*, Friday, January 31, 1964 . . .")

("DR. KING PROPOSED FOR NOBEL PRIZE. Stockholm, Jan. 30, 1964 (Reuters)—Eight Swedish members of Parliament today nominated the Rev. Dr. Martin Luther

King, Jr., the American Negro integrationist leader, as a candidate for the 1964 Nobel Peace Prize, the Swedish News Agency reported today. In a letter to the Norwegian Nobel Committee, they said Dr. King, who has led American Negroes in their fight for equality since 1955, 'had succeeded in keeping his followers to the principle of nonviolence . . .' ")

(The Commuter: A Day in August, Washington D.C. —If the assassination of President Kennedy was like televised Greek tragedy, then the opening act for me took place that hot August day of the Freedom March in Washington. I had just arrived in Washington that morning; the day before I was in Rome. Now I was shoulder to shoulder with the marchers, thousands and thousands of smiling brown and white faces, moving slowly like a sluggish river of humanity toward the white marble isolation of the Lincoln Monument. Abraham Lincoln was dead. But his statue there at the monument was at least twenty times the height of the flesh-and-blood freedmen marching to be free. We are clean, well-groomed, self-consciously well-behaved. Slouching policemen watch us as we sing: "We shall overcome someday . . ." Government buildings are closed for the day (as are the liquor stores), but ghostly faces peer down at us from upper-story windows. Little by little, though, the initial feeling of triumph and exhilaration begins to fade. I become an intellectual again, my critical faculties become alert, and I can no longer join in the holding of hands and the singing. Suddenly an insidious cynical voice begins whispering in my ear that what I am witnessing, participating in, is only a summer pageant of brotherhood, some strange new hybrid form of political manifestation, a kind of animated advertising slogan, a "revolution" only by name. By this time I have become conscious of the countless television cameras along the route. And I cannot help but note how every time a group of marchers approaches one of these television cameras the marchers straighten up and assume "revolutionary" poses, and boisterously break out into song. Obviously history *was* being made that hot day in August in Washington, D.C. But who was making it? We, the marchers? The gray and blue uniformed drivers of those sleek diesel buses who with such logistical efficiency had transported bodily the thousands and thousands of brown and white faced marchers to Washington? The gum-chewing cigar-smoking cameramen perched on their mobile platforms of iron pipe behind the electronic eyes of the television cameras? Then it was that a terrible doubt began to creep into my mind: Is this Event taking place because of the television cameras, or are the television cameras here because of the Event? This, I suppose, is only a contemporary version of that most ancient of theatrical riddles: What is true and what is illusion? But if history now is to become televised theatre, where are we the intellectuals to stand? In the audience? On the stage? Or in the prompter's cramped and dusty pit?

Theatrically, historically, the assassination of John Fitzgerald Kennedy was a terrible mistake . . .)

But now, as I sit here in Doris' low-ceilinged living room, once the house-steward's quarters of this siege-proof prisonlike princely palace in Rome, I keep asking myself just exactly what it is that has made the Doris sitting opposite me, her long lathe-tapered legs in swan-like repose, as outside the narrow lace-curtained window the vesper bells toll and someone nervously guns the motor of a Lambretta, and a dog with a throat ailment barks with unconvincing mournfulness, so different from the Doris who came bouncing with such joyful violence into my studio, seemingly centuries and centuries ago, that reckless day of sunswept astrological beginnings, how many years ago in 196-, when I condescendingly informed her, this Doris maiden of unknown historical roots, that I, the Writer, had decided to *write a novel* about *her* . . .

She is, of course, the same person, this Doris of mine. That is, her name is still Doris, and the silken rose-brown involucre containing her flesh and vital organs, the unembalmable transistorized memory of her cells, is the same; she is a figment of my imagination, this Doris of mine, no less than are we all the figments of imagination of those who, whether out of love or hate or boredom, in the gloomy waiting rooms of railway or subway stations, or inside that ever-expanding, that ever-clouded fishbowl waiting room of Life, which is our existence now and here on this planet, do take the time to observe us, turn the flashlight of their "busy" consciousnesses on us, and, by means of that known-forever-known laser ray of love or simple attention, overcome our chronic doubt, convince us that we too are real and thus *reale*, Doris is a figment of my imagination—and yet she too, no less than all and everything of us, animate or inanimate, organic or inorganic, pedestrian or shade, no less than all of us, and everything we are, the worlds we inhabit, the worlds that inhabit us, no less than the changeless immutable law itself, Doris too must conform, must submit, to that most sacred of universal laws, that first and only law which forever has taught, shall in all eternity teach, that life is existence and existence is sacred, that now-forgotten sacred law that governs the dance hall and traffic, the tidal flow of rivers and volcanic lakes, the gestation cycle of pregnant squids, the migration of birds, the migration of undesirable peoples (yellow-brown-black-and-white-all-are-precious-in-his-sight), that governs the universe, the Univac, the timing of aging TV comedians' electronically-inserted laughs, that solemn rock-bottom law of Transformation (or plastically, three-dimensionally, Transmutation), the (for we human-brained and human-eyed monsters, the sea-gull scavengers of the crumbs and garbage or potential perception) embarrassing, the terrifying, the unembalmable law of changeless change . . .

A pompous, self-indulgent way of saying that Doris has changed, is no longer the Nubian handmaiden of Elizabeth Taylor in the Twentieth Century-Fox production of *Cleopatra*, filmed in Rome centuries and centuries ago. Doris, the Doris wearing a striped prisoner's tunic, this chain-gang Doris, is not bursting, exploding with exuberance and joy, she has become a princess from the Orient, cool and elusive, light of weight, the sunset rays suddenly now have turned her flesh a cosmetically winter-garden shade of the nightshade flower, this rose color I saw with my own eyes on the foot-worn floor of the Cathedral of Siena.

This Doris, then, has changed, has become:
Catherine of Siena, Margherita of Cortona, Irene of Poland, the *"fanciulla"* of Grottarossa, the ghost of Laura . . . I read today that Clare Boothe Luce wants to become President of the United States. (My wife, Tatina, says that this is an "exaggeration.") This second day of Lent there is much talk, in the newspapers and the cafés, of mummies and gold and incense and myrrh and linen swathing, Paul Getty, the richest man in the world bought in 1938, so *Time* magazine says, a painting of Raffaello of "The Madonna of Loreto." I have been to that church on the Adriatic coast. Tambroni, now dead, was the Minister of the Marine. I was there on the Adriatic coast as a journalist to write about the "Fair of Fishing and the Merchant Marine." I remember the warmth of that church, situated on a tiny hill. All we journalists ate deliciously prepared fish. I visited the house of the poet Leopardi, he is dead. I entered his library, on the steps of Leopardi's house Ugo Moretti and I had our photographs taken. Two nights ago I prayed to the Madonna of Loreto. Alex laughed when I told him. And yet it is such a rich experience to pray to the many many

madonnas of Rome. Here in Italy, sailors and trainmen and policemen and stevedores pray to madonnas. In America we don't. In America we pray to the Lord. Why?

"Where were you when it happened?"

"I was not *there*. I was not in Dallas. I was in New York . . ."

"November 22. The Count called me up and told me. I was writing a letter to my mother . . ."

"Paul Getty is the richest man in the world. In 1938 he bought a crusty old Italian painting which just recently they have discovered is an authentic Raffaello. It is a painting of the Madonna of Loreto. Behind the Madonna there stands a Man. The Man stands in shadows. I forget now whether or not the Man has a beard . . ."

"The Count's name is Raffaele. It is a name I like to pronounce . . . Raffaele . . ."

"Raffaello died a young man. His work was not finished. Michelangelo lived to be an old man. Michelangelo was less sensitive they say, Michelangelo had a beard. The man standing in the shadows of Paul Getty's 'Madonna of Loreto' looks very much like Michelangelo . . ."

"There are so many madonnas in Rome, in Italy . . . People pray to them. But I never have. Kennedy was a Catholic. Do you think that is why they killed him?"

"No one knows. Or if they know, they do not say. The week he was assassinated, an anonymous gunman in New York shot a girl who was getting ready to go to bed. He shot her with a high-powered rifle, in the darkness, he stood on railway tracks and shot her in the back . . ."

"The Madonna of Loreto is the patroness of aviators . . ."

"On TV, you had no feeling of death. Of the President stabbed by Brutus in the back. The TV screen was too small for the idea of Death and Love, of Generous Presiding . . . The black, gray and white images had not enough tints and colors for the idea of the absence of lymph and bloody green growing into maturity and understanding of the terrible role of being, presiding, sitting in the hot seat of power. They could not get this idea over through electronically mystery-movie-type TV images. Marconi, afloat on his river Styx ship, smiled then. There was high-fidelity sound. Into our tiny urban renewal apartment, with B.K. and my sister, both admiring the efficiency of it all, what great administrators are we ladies and girls, came the sound waves ciphered in homely similar homes by Mozart and Beethoven, music came and wrapped itself around our big city perversity, our big city cult of aloneness, music brought another kind of warmth to still the rising temperature of criminal delight, the bang-bang-you're-dead of criminal child-play journalism on film . . . I was so grateful for the music of Mozart and Beethoven, I do not like the mirror-reflected images of urban civilization on the miserable two-by-four TV screen. We are greater. We are bigger. Christ walked with big steps, left big footsteps, his fingerprints are like geological maps. Why did they assassinate you, Mr. Kennedy, my Lord? Some say they assassinated you because you did not wear a hat. The University of Padova, the University of Harvard, service must never be secret, generosity must not be punished but praised, shall we all now become assassins? The assassins of John Wilkes Booth? My editor friend didn't go back to his office, he said he was going home—but where was home?—to his Manhattan flat, to change his clothes. Two days later I was seated in a shabby hotdog stand on Broadway when I saw small crowds of people gathered about parked automobiles, or unemployed youths wearing sharp-pointed shoes carrying transistor radios, I ate a second hotdog, then I sidled up to yet another crowd of people inside a women's wear shop of some kind on Forty-second Street and finally asked, 'What's going on?' 'President Kennedy has been assassinated.' An elegant Jewish youth looked at me, observed my reaction. Time was swallowed up into some terrifying hole. I have never seen Kennedy. I found myself on a bus headed for home, up Fifth Avenue. Girls were streaming into Saint Patrick's. Office workers poured out of the shining brass skyscraper doors of Big Corporations. There was silence and fear. Many wept. Tears come to me only if I weep about—Big Cities are not sophisticated. New York suddenly began to menstruate. Suddenly New York was like a hysterical old maid who has suddenly learned that the menopause—Death—does indeed exist . . ."

(*"Spotlight on Psychiatry* . . . RUBY TRIAL STARTS
TODAY; MAY BECOME U.S. CLASSIC. Dallas, Feb. 16, 1964
(API)—When Jack Ruby steps into Court tomorrow he
will be the principal figure in a murder case promising to
become an American classic. Ruby's chief counsel, Mel-
vin Belli of San Francisco, has indicated he may try to go
fully into all the evidence surrounding President John F.
Kennedy's assassination as a necessary part of Ruby's
defense. Ruby killed Lee Harvey Oswald, Mr. Kennedy's
accused assassin, with a snub-nosed .38-caliber pistol in
the basement of Dallas' City Hall last November 24. Mr.
Belli said last week: 'This is a historical case. The most
important aspect of it will be psychiatric testimony. Everyone saw Ruby shoot Oswald—a national television
audience watched—but no one saw into this man's
mind' . . .")

"It was only after I got back to New York from
Washington and Atlantic City last September that the
idea, the theory of this narration, this chronicle, this
journey of ours through time and space, became clearer
in my mind. In Washington and Atlantic City summer
was coming to an end. Everything was slow and suspended, crystalline and obvious, like a brightly lit tab-
leau against a sky-blue backdrop. But once in New
York, the long Labor Day weekend and the Freedom
March already washed away to another dimension of
memory, subtly the weather changed, and with it the
weather within our minds. Over the Atlantic, north and
south, raged wild restless hurricanes, bearing the names

(207)

of girls. Erratically, defying the laws of weather prediction, the hurricanes roamed fickly, north and south, east and west. On the early morning television programs and on the evening news summaries, the weather commentators designed neurotic childlike scribblings on the weather charts, to indicate the strangeness of the hurricanes' paths. I took a pretty college girl home from a party, we bought a heavy loaded copy of the *New York Times*, and she told me as we approached her brownstone house just off Central Park West, that in the room beneath hers there lived an active member of the American Nazi Party, and that he kept a large supply of dynamite under his bed. How did she know? When I told her that I was looking for a job in New York, that I had applied for a job at Standard Oil of New Jersey, the firm my father has been connected with for over forty years, among other places, she seemed scandalized and asked me if I were 'selling out to the other side.' Of course it was useless to say that I was not selling out, that I had nothing to sell, that I was only looking for a job in New York.

"What I mean, though, is simply this. That everything and everybody, real or invented, characters in books or in newspapers, the 'news' itself, stones and broken bottles *do* matter, *are* important, if only they are looked at, if only they are observed, just because they are composed of matter. Because everything and everybody, real or invented, characters in books, even the books themselves, even the book jacket and the colored ink on the cover design, is composed of matter and for this reason matters, must therefore breathe in harmony with a single governing law, respond according to its aliveness, its *alertness*, to the degree that it is awake or awakened, to the shifting humors of the wind-tormented involucre of our physical environment, which through Penelope's law of tapestry, Penelope's law of changeless change, can, as so often it does, become transmuted into climate and weather, weather peaceful or calm, these wild pregnant storm signals that flash ignored through our minds . . ."

(Today is Sunday, February 23, 1964. Here in Rome it is a gray ashen day. We are today in Lent, the city is tense, its marble fingers are clenched, the sky is low and heavy on the brow of the Seven Hills, the seasonal Mystery Play has begun, the inaudible chants, the distant blowing of ram's-horn trumpets has frightened the dogs, two this morning, I saw them with my own eyes, roamed the streets without master or pastor, some vandal has drawn with a red pencil a phallic prick and balls over the doorbell of our apartment, I am glad, thankful, though secretly alarmed, that the phallic prick and balls is not a Star of David nor a swastika symbol of Persian sun, I am thankful for many things, today in Rome, this gray ashen day of Lent, thankful for the mood of mystery, of austerity, of Lent, thankful that the city breathes and sobs, childishly fights back the tears of grief and bell-ringing joy. March 27, Good Friday, March 29, Easter, on March 30 I shall fly back to New York on an Alitalia plane, on April 1, St. Ugo Bishop, I shall begin work at the advertising agency, today the city sorrows but tears do not come, I left the house early, what a strangely and typically Roman sight to see streetcleaners and old women porters sweeping, solemn and Gregorian the rhythm of their strokes, witch-broom elegy of the seasonal Mystery to come, FIAT, not the automobile, but in Latin "that it should come," the Event, the Advent, here in Rome this gray ashen day of Lent, we wait, we are children, we know the story, Beginning, Middle, End, we wait, the sky fights to hold back its tears which cannot, shall not, come, only snow, we wait to weep when the Prompter gives the cue, children are we, Our Father Who Art in Heaven, Hallowed be Thy Name, there was a police car in Piazza Mazzini this morning when the two masterless, pastorless dogs trotted neuroticly down the street, the same police car was parked in front of the baretto where I have coffee, where my son has Coca-Cola, where my mother-in-law, who took a bath this morning and looked like a fifteen-year-old girl, she refuses to lock the bathroom door, reads *Il Messaggero*, my friend, the artist from Calabria, Rotella, whose collages give me a desperate tangible touchable feeling of here and now in Rome, who *tears* not in anger but with the neurotic compulsion of the caged exile seeking spiritual peace, this Rotella friend of mine who is on and inside the very first page of this novel has been arrested, Rotella this gray ashen day of Lent in Rome is in jail, the police have arrested this artist friend of mine for use of or trafficking in drugs or marijuana, we talked that New Year's Day of 1963 of the *danger*, Rotella showed me a Buddha which the Far Eastern archaeologist Tucci had given him, or perhaps a friend of Professor Tucci's, that day Rotella was afraid, he said that in the year 1963 he would either live or he would die, I bought a "painting," a collage, which together we entitled, because of a phrase on one of the Roman public notices included in the touchable tangible design, "La Tessera della Povertà," which means "The Poor Man's Identity Card," and on the back of the collage, Rotella wrote and dedicated the following poem:

> *Dal Passaporto di*
> *Povertà,*
> *Alla Tessera*
> *Del Dalai Lama,*
> *Per Bill,*
> *Nell'Anno*
> *Novo-Realista,*
> *1963*

It is a quarter to one. I hope that Rotella in Queen of Heaven jail is having a good Sunday meal, I hope the meal consists of spaghetti and roast chicken, I sincerely hope this Calabrian artist friend of mine, who came to our carnival children's party last year and recited his "*epistaltica*" poetry and recorded on his tape recorder the Applause Contest, in which I told the costumed children that we adults, especially those who work in the field of Art, are hungry, are starved for applause, and that I would give a first, second and third prize to those children present at the party who would praise and applaud me the loudest, oh, how intoxicating was that praise and that applause, sufficient it was for a lifetime, so sincerely I hope that Rotella, this Calabrian artist friend of mine, soon is freed, "La Tessera della Povertà" is the *quadro* I shall meditate on, this ashen gray Sunday of Lent . . .)

"You see, Doris, our country is sick. America is sick. I remember, Doris, the day, perhaps in 1961 or 1962, it doesn't matter, I rose very early in the morning, with my wife, to go with J.P. and Laura, you remember Laura, who committed suicide, and Mangione and Mangione's daughter, who looks like Stefania Sandrelli in *Seduced and Abandoned*, to see the eclipse; as dawn radiated a cold pink sadness over the Via Cassia landscape going north from Rome, a desolate bitter landscape scarred by wave after wave of invasions from the north, in two automobiles, Laura's Citroën and Mario's coffin-white Fiat roadster-speedster, we went to a certain place, a little more than an hour's drive from Rome, to witness a terrifying event, to witness that which only strong spirits should dare to witness.

Never never never shall I forget that terrifying moment when the sun was no more, when an underworld sea-bottom glow rippled across the field, and I felt cold and cold-blooded, a creature of the sea, an exile from sacred evolution, there were colors to that rippling glow but colors that had no names in the vocabulary or literature of advertising, it was cold, it was evil, Someone, something else, reigned in that eternal moment of the unholy spectacle of the moon overshadowing the blazing glory of the sun, the Son, there was a busload of girl students come to witness this advent of He who reigns beneath and within, they turned their faces, hid their faces in their hands and made strange sounds, they tried to look away, this, I guess, was the mystical moment of Elevation, the elevation of that which is not, the anti-of-the-antis, the astronomical justification of the Anti-Christ . . .

"But I did not mean to talk about that eclipse, Doris, we were talking about America last fall, the sickness of America, why this long shadow over America. How long will this sickness last?"

"Americans often say: 'This is God's Country'?"

"What really do they mean, Doris? Do they mean that God carries an American passport? Yesterday, Sunday, I went to visit Alex, I returned to him a Philips radio we bought together in our bohemian days some fourteen years ago in an appliance store near Piazza di Venezia, the radio's brown plastic box has been shattered and clumsily pieced back together, the light of its dial still glows with a yellow-green brightness like a lightning bug in the purple garden of a moonlit summer night, but the tubes—how much has happened in fourteen years, chain reaction of technical progress, tubes are no longer tubes but the transistorized scratching of a labyrinth of memory upon a plastic plaque; I remember searching for sound and speeches and music from what was then called the ether by scratching a crystal nugget with the whisker of a cat—no longer work, Alex again declared himself an atheist, said that I was incurably sentimental to believe in God and religion, to pray to madonnas; said I: What difference does it make if one is a believer or an atheist, if God exists or does not exist? One believes or does not believe, one knows or one does not know, sophisticated arguments can defend or demolish the thesis that Ruby, the assassin of the presumed assassin, is sane or insane. What is Evil? I asked Alex, my oldest friend in Rome, and Alex said that though he himself had personally never experienced Evil, Alex said that he *knew* what Evil was, Alex said that Evil was the enjoyment of someone else's suffering and pain . . .

"You see, Doris, our country is suffering, America is sick. But what we don't know yet is the nature of this sickness. What *is* America's sickness? If only my brother, Frank, were here, he would tell me. That day toward the end of the war when he appeared in the entrance of my tent, I was near Grosseto, in Etruscan country, he took me to his camp, Torre del Lago, where Puccini lived and composed, onyx-black was the still volcanic lake when my brother Frank placed a machine gun in my hand and told me to shoot, *mitragliatrice,* I was ashamed of the intoxicating joy of firing, lacerating the stillness and quiet of that Tuscan night, *rat-a-ta-ta-ta-ta-ta-ta,* two years later, a student at Fisk University, I bought an album of Puccini's *La Bohème,* and would turn the phonograph thunderously loud, '*Che gelida manina,*' today in 1964 my brother Frank is a staff physician at a state mental hospital in San Francisco, first he was a pharmacologist, then he became a specialist in internal medicine, now his specialization is geriatrics! Were he here with me now, my brother Frank, I would ask: Is America's sickness, the sickness of America today, a sickness of childhood, chicken pox, German measles, scarlet fever, a sickness of adolescence, a sickness of romantic love and breathing and lungs, tuberculosis in a new and more virulent form, or is the sickness of our country the sickness of old age, arthritis and senility, palsy? I would ask my brother: Frank, why is our country sick?

"So, after the funeral for our assassinated President, there was this strange provincial reception in the White House for all those heads and vice-heads of states, kings and dukes and queens and prime ministers and emperors from Europe and its provinces, who like doctors on some terrifyingly urgent emergency call, interrupted their card games and private lessons in Japanese, came rushing to Washington, their peacock private planes landing at lonely Dulles Airport, to bring order to the tragic hour of the child rebel nation whose doll has fallen and fractured its head, to bring, like minor Magi, to offer with measured phrases and diplomatic smiles and private colognes and scents, the fruit of centuries and centuries of poisonings and political intrigue, the cutting off of heads, high Masses in Gothic cathedrals, the ritual of condolence and the conversion of state jewels into cash, the European quadrille of governing, well and bad, but always the raising to a higher power of that ballet-school perfection of hypocrisy, tempered now in this muddy neoclassic place of Washington, D.C., by a TV-spied-upon fear of nuclear war, an earthquake on the island of São Jorge in the Portugese Azores roused 20,000 inhabitants from their sleep and sent them fleeing from becoming extras in yet another rehash of *The Lost Continent of Atlantis*, the fruit of centuries and centuries of Learning and Experience and Civilization, bows and curtsies and the right tie in the right palace and the right crossing of the aristocratic leg in the politically leftish parlor, the clanking of medals, each head and vice-head of government or state, each king and duke and queen and minister, rare and prime, each visiting doctor on this emergency call from Europe and the provinces of that distant fairyland, each bemedaled muddled emissary missionary brought us a word of comfort in our moment of distress, hinted at a diagnosis of the malady now become critical for the ailing giant of Democracy, as glasses clinked and television cameras whirred, whispered knowingly of infallible cures, cures excogitated by reptilian-blooded court physicians with headquarters in the basements of overseas banks, oh, they came in great numbers, Doris, the ruling heads of Europe, with my sister Dorothy, and B.K., munching on cheese and crackers and drinking imported Norwegian beer, we watched them crowd self-consciously, herded and intimidated by the heat of the TV floodlights, perspiring beneath their rustling silks and silk underwear and uneasy over lack of toilet facilities, heads of states, kings and dukes and queens and ministers, rare and prime, though advanced in age, have not the same toilet privileges as do the pupils of a well-organized private or public school, the funeral procession to Arlington Cemetery was long and, because funereal, very very slow, I had occasion to go to the bathroom twice during the duration of that funeral procession, the horses could relieve themselves, in time-hallowed cavalry tradition, along the monumental avenue, and the Negroes and whites crowded along the route would not, could not, be scandalized, unless perhaps the horse nervously prancing behind the cannons and mounted honor guards, the shiny-polished riding academy horse with the empty saddle were to relieve himself, but the doctors from Europe had no such toilet privileges, and we watched their strained faces as they tried to be condolent, tried to analyze the shattering problems of the ailing giant of Democracy in distress, but, frankly, Doris, just between you and me, there was only one thing on their mind, on the minds of the heads of state from Europe and the provinces of Europe: I must hold it in, I must give proof and evidence, here in this quiet barbarous place of doll-house neoclassic, this place where only through the intervention of Merlin, King Arthur's court magician, the olden buks of Law and Human Rights are custodied, not the Holy Grail, that is in that other place, I must smile under the heat of the TV floodlights, I must be disciplined lest my dancing master become scandalized and angry, I must above all smile and be nonchalant before the millions and millions of emigrant traitors who refused to pay their taxes on tea and salt, the vulgar ex-jailbirds, whores, indentured workers, clodhoppers, wops, slaves and degenerate African kings, I must smile and be nonchalant before this mass of what they so arrogantly call themselves, Americans, I must hold it in, hold it in (burp!), I must hold it in and give proof and evidence of my European Culture and Civilization, if only there were not so many of us crowded into this tiny room, if only General De Gaulle would get here—is he taller than the new president?— why did President Johnson hold onto the hand of that emperor from Ethiopia so long? . . . And the TV cameras whirred, recording this strangely urgent marathon of mind over intestine and kidney, I must smile and be nonchalant, I must hold it in, the impartial objective electronic eye put it all down on sensitivized tape, we watched, munching cheese and crackers and drinking imported Norwegian beer, my sister Dorothy and B.K., in that tiny flat off Ninety-sixth Street, we watched the events of history move with shadowy logic across the tiny TV screen, while the riderless horse, the frisky colt from Pakistan, was eating its oats, and the young President was dead and buried, assassinated before having had the time even to grow an Abraham Lincoln beard . . ."

"CLAY WINS IN 7 AS LISTON HURTS SHOULDER. Miami Beach, Feb. 26, 1964—Undefeated Cassius Clay perpetrated one of the incredible upsets of boxing history last night when the seemingly indestructible Sonny Liston failed to come out for the seventh round of their world heavyweight title bout. It was recorded as a technical knockout in the seventh round . . . 'I'm the Greatest, I'm the King of the World!' Cassius Clay shouted in near hysteria after his victory over Liston . . .")

("Clay, Cassius Marcellus, 1810-1903, American politician, was born in Madison County, Kentucky, on October 19, 1810. He was a son of Green Clay, 1757-1826, a Kentucky soldier of the War of 1812 and a relative of Henry Clay. He was educated at Centre College in Danville, Kentucky, and at Yale, where he graduated in 1832. Influenced to some extent by William Lloyd Garrison, he became an advocate of the abolition of slavery . . .")

(Today is Friday, February 28, 1964, I have finally outlined the ending of the novel, my wife agrees that while it is indeed an exciting ending for the novel, she would prefer not being included in the final imaginary scene, I have just come back from my afternoon walk in the vicinity of Via Margutta and Piazza di Spagna, I met the gnomelike old lady who was the "doorman" of the building on Via Margutta where I first met Alex, I saw our old friend Renzo Vespignani, plump and prosperous, owning now an Alfa Romeo, a sharp new young girl friend, building a villa on Lake Bracciano, his paintings selling like dollar bills, talking to an art dealer just off Via Babuino, with a sudden pang of nostalgia, I recalled those happy days in the attic apartment on Via San Teodoro when Muccini, who has an excellent show going now in a gallery in Piazza di Spagna, he has three mistresses to support, Vespignani and Graziella, the girl friend he has discarded, or perhaps the other way around, Alex and I and Wolfgang Frankl's two Arcadianly lovely daughters were living an authentic bohemian life, cats and fireplaces and the Roman Forum within spitting distance across the narrow cobblestoned street, and yet I am happy to be returning to New York, I think . . .)

(" 'GOD HELPED ME BEAT LISTON,' CLAY SAYS HE HAS ADOPTED ISLAM, 'A WAY OF LIFE THAT WILL SAVE THE WORLD.' Miami Beach, Feb. 27, 1964—The new heavyweight boxing champion of the world, Cassius Clay, said today he had adopted the Islam religion and regarded it as the best way to bring about lasting peace among the peoples of the world . . . 'They call it the Black Muslims,' the 22-year-old fighter said. 'This is a press word. It is not a legitimate name. But Islam is a religion and there are 750 million people all over the world who believe in it, and I am one of them . . .' The new champion said he believed that his new-found religion, 'which has brought me a great inner peace,' was largely responsible for his victory over Sonny Liston . . . 'God was with me. He guided me all the way. He helped me to beat that big, ugly bear that everybody said could not be beaten.'

... Clay said that he was disturbed that the Islam religion had been referred to as a Communist and hate group ... 'We don't hate anyone. We love everybody,' he said.")

(The doorbell rings. Doris gets up to answer it. From the narrow hallway a throaty female voice says in Italian: "*Ti vogliono al telefono* ..." Doris appears momentarily in the doorway of the room where we have been sitting and talking and says: "Someone wants me on the phone downstairs. I haven't been able to get a phone installed in this place yet. Make yourself at home, I'll be right back ..."

I am tempted to snoop around. And after less than a minute's debate with my conscience, that is exactly what I do. Instinctively, I first go to the bathroom. Perhaps to justify my presence there, I pretend to urinate, but my bladder is empty. On top of the medicine cabinet there are a large furry teddy bear and a freshly opened package of Kleenex. There is a half inch of bluish soap-filmed water in the bidet. A pair of silk stockings and a perspiration-stained white nylon brassiere are drip-drying over the narrow rusty bathtub. The hot water heater, an old-fashioned gas-burning contraption, obviously has not worked for years. There is a sewerlike stench in the absurdly cramped bathroom as though the toilet drain is clogged. But there is also, like the counterpoint of a fugue, the trilling upper-register scent of expensive perfume. On the white enamel toilet box there is a three-week-old copy of the *Rome Daily American*, with the front page torn diagonally, isolating the inch-high word

CYPRUS. A cockroach appears from beneath a small but extremely effective electric heater with a German trade name. I start to crush it under my foot, but change my mind, and sheepishly leave the bathroom, strangely embarrassed by the lonely squalor.

(Today is Monday, March 2, 1964, it is 6:30 P.M., my son is happily in bed, recovering from an attack of flu, he is playing with the tape recorder that was his favorite Epiphany gift, half an hour ago my wife received from a retired army colonel an advance payment for the sale of the vineyard I bought during a period of spiritual crisis, almost as a frantic gesture to feel rooted somewhere on this earth, I stole into the kitchen to ask Emma for a glass of wine, I found her standing before the calendar of the parish of the Sacred Heart of Christ the King, she did not hear me enter the kitchen, I watched as she stuck a pearl-headed pin through the dates of March 29, Easter Sunday, and March 30, Easter Monday, the day I shall board an Alitalia plane and fly back to New York in time to begin work at the advertising agency, the morning of April the first. In the *Herald Tribune,* I read: "President Johnson disclosed yesterday that the United States has secretly developed a 2,000-mile-an-hour jet fighter which performs at altitudes of more than 70,000 feet. He said its performance 'far exceeds that of any other aircraft in the world today . . .' ")

(Today is Tuesday, March 3, 1964, the instant that our son came, as he always does, every morning, tiptoeing into the bedroom to share the special warmth of the father-mother bed, I was having a dream, a dream in a pink and golden glow, of the Chase Manhattan Bank, the building was a heavy-columned interpretation of neo-classic architecture, but with an enormous window occupying almost the entire wall, and in the window were huge ledgers, bound in precious leather, all in order on row after row of bookshelves, but one book was lying horizontally atop the other books on the top shelf, and only on this book could I make out any words, the title of this book in the pink and golden glow of my dream was: *Horse Shoe . . .*)

I should not do this but I pick up the unfinished letter on Doris' desk and read: "Dear Father—" But immediately I am distracted. Angry voices penetrate the silence of the apartment. Upstairs or downstairs a man and a woman are quarreling. She is saying: *"Sei un carogna!"* He is saying: *"Eri tu . . . eri tu!"* And suddenly it seems that the racetrack rhythm of the motor bikes and automobiles on the street below have speeded up, at the same time the silence inside Doris' apartment has become almost tactile, the cheap writing paper of the letter in my hand crackles as though charged with electricity . . .

(Today is Thursday, March 5, 1964. On March 5, 1962, I began this narration. That day there was bright sunlight in Rome. Today it rains. Rome is depressed and listless. There are too many people walking the streets in the rain. This is a sign of economic crisis. Men are ashamed to be at home when their manhood is threatened by the loss of jobs. I too took my afternoon walk in the rain. I met Francine Virduzzo who told me that the new issue of *New Morality* is out, that this issue, with my article about the Freedom March and the assassination of Kennedy, is a "*cannonata.*" I met Vespignani who did not recognize me at first and then I realized that his jaw was swollen with a terrible toothache. Then, strangely, but appropriately, I saw the young aristocrat who is on page 7 of the narration. I have not seen him since the time, two years ago, he appeared on television to tell of his experiences in Algeria during the closing weeks of the Algerian war. He was not wearing a raincoat. It had stopped raining by then. His hair has become thinner. He seemed preoccupied, seemed to be talking to himself. I did not hail him, he was on the other side of the street . . .)

(But the season now grows late. In less than three weeks time I will be flying back to New York. From their underground resting place the restless ghosts of the swindled Iroquois and the Dutch swindlers will breathe Central Park's sweeter deeper green. It will be April in New York, flowers will bloom like tiny girl college students in the forgotten cemeteries of Trinity Church and the Church of the Intercession. The cranky cantankerous Lexington Avenue subway will suddenly run on time. I will sit at a desk in my skyscraper office, I will work to the rhythm of the Easter-Parade resurrected city. Smoothly but with green swiftness will flow the deep rivers that hold Manhattan in their sexually awakened maternal embrace. The season here in Rome grows late.

It is time for me to leave, I must bring this strange chaotic narration to its untrue, its unreal, its literally fictionized end. So it is that I stand here now, leaning against a blanket-covered desk, in Doris' tiny apartment, in the servants' quarters of a princely palace, in the criminal gloom of Via Giulia, about to read a letter she had begun but not ended, a letter to her father. Stiffening my muscles, so as to shut out the distracting shrill voices coming from the trombonelike staircase outside the door, I again force my attention to the urgent defiant scrawl: "Dear Father . . ."

"Dear Father," I read, "In Rome it has begun to rain . . ."

(Doris is on her way up the stairs. In a few minutes she will push her way angrily through whatever the nonsensical Roman quarrel is going on in the trombonish servants' quarters staircase, she will burst into the room and affront me, but first I pause to glance at my *New York Herald Tribune*, today is Monday, March 9, 1964, yesterday the Day of the Emancipated Woman in Rome, my wife shouted angrily that all we foreign invaders of the Italian patria are Germans, but I am Dutch, this narration is a Dutch treat, I have the feeling that here in Rome it is the first day of spring, at the tobacco store in Piazza di Spagna where I go always to buy my fresh-minted copy of the *New York Herald Tribune*, a froggish Roman small businessman asked, as though the foreigners were again going to put something over on him, narrow his customer-cheating potentiality, "When is Easter this year?" so in Dick Tracy, the following dialogue, no, it is a monologue, I now realize, for only Dick Tracy's chic girl friend is speaking, speaking about the radar-horned "Moon Maiden":

"The sun is restoring her power . . ."
"Look! She's getting back to normal. She kicked her blanket away!"
"Her powers are coming back fast!"
"I wonder how she'd look in a cute little frock!"

And also I read, but suddenly how bored I have become: FLOYD WOULD FIGHT 'CASSIUS X' FOR NOTHING—IN ORDER TO WREST TITLE FROM BLACK MUSLIMS . . .

Says Floyd Patterson, former heavyweight champion of the world, who lost the title to Sonny Liston in a previous chapter of this narration: if only the Sicilian-Americans would make up their minds whether they are in love with the Teuton Templars or the Mustached Saracen Pirates; says Floyd Patterson, according to the fighting press: "I disagree with the precepts of the Black Muslims, just as I disagree with the Ku Klux Klan—in fact so much so, I am willing and desire to fight Cassius X to take the title from the Black Muslim leadership and will do so for no purse whatsoever, whenever and wherever they might desire . . ."

"What don't you remember? What don't you recall? And what are you doing, snooping around reading my letters?"

"Oh, Doris, I didn't hear you come in . . ."

"Always snooping around, reading other peoples' letters, snooping into their minds. I hate you, I hate writers, worse of all I hate Negro writers, you and Jimmy Baldwin included!"

"But, Doris, what does Jimmy Baldwin have to do with us?"

"Everything! Our people shouldn't be writers. We're different. We shouldn't try to put things down in words! Let white people write things down. I wish the Count were a writer instead of you! I wish you were a Count instead of a writer!"

(The Count has just returned to his office from the discreet coffee bar on Via Bissolati where he had gone to telephone Doris, safe from the snooping ears of his British colleague, Higgins, who now looks up from his copy of the *New York Herald Tribune* and comments with a sly missionary smile on his bloodless lips: "Well. I told you so!"

"What?"

"I told you Patterson would try to make a comeback on the good Christian, against the bad Muslim bit!"

"But Sonny Liston had been saved from being a jailbird by Catholic priests, if I am not mistaken . . ."

"My dear Count, the blood of noble Crusaders runs in your veins, but not the blood of us hard-headed British and Sicilian businessmen! Unfortunately, you are not an islander, you are and always will be an outlander, you

(2 2 7)

have no sense of business, and boxing, like crime and the baking of bread, has become, for better or for worse, Big Business . . ."

"Apparently Religion, if I understand you correctly, has also become Big Business . . ."

"Religion has always been Big Business, the biggest Big Business—otherwise so many excellent criminal minds would not be attracted to the field. But that is not what I am talking about. No longer being able to pit the White Man against the Black Man, we must stage our colossal spectacles in a strange exciting new light— religion against religion! My God, what possibilities for the British and Sicilian promoters! And how appropriate that they are transferring you to Hong Kong! The Japanese Olympics! The winner of the Fight of Fights, Christian against Muslim, will take on the Champion of Buddhism! The possibilities are simply staggering! What religion will in the end prevail?"

"The religion of Death—"

"Oh, you *are* in a bad mood today, my dear Count. Why don't you phone your little *Faccetta Nera* from here in the office? I personally can assure you that, at this hour of the day, our phones are not tapped . . ."

"Higgins . . . I know you are a friend. We have worked together now for something like thirteen years. But I still don't understand you, in spite of what kind of blood courses through my veins. I must tell you this, even though you shall not, cannot understand, you have a commercial mind, this Italian sun has not yet succeeded in unchilling your heart, but I am deeply in love with 'Faccetta Nera,' as you call her, and at the same time, or perhaps because I am in love with Doris, I have become even more deeply in love with my wife! Now how do you explain that? And please put down the newspaper barrier between us, *if we are to speak together, at last,* after all these years of sharing almost the same desk, talk man-to-man! . . ."

"Somewhere in that strange literary review you showed me the other day, there was a quote from William of Orange: *'Il n'y a pas besoin d'espérer pour entreprendre, ni de réussir pour persévérer . . .'*"

"Am I correct in assuming that what you were trying to say, before you brought my remote ancestor, William of Orange, spouting inanities in French, into the question, that religion is the biggest of Big Business, because we are fallen angels, because the road back to Paradise is long and arduous, the tariff, by plane, camel, broom or donkey, is high—even though we of the aircraft business shall on April first radically reduce our rates—because the speculators along the long and arduous route back to our lost Paradise are legion, the cost of a lemonade or a watered-down beer extremely high?"

"Theology, my dear Count! They are wise indeed to send you to Hong Kong, where there is no Theology, only Business . . . Strange they didn't send you to New York for the Exposition of Michelangelo's 'Pietà.' Now what religion would you say a piece of sculpture like that represents?"

"Now that you ask me, Michelangelo's 'Pietà' never gave me the feeling of—"

"Of what, my dear Count, what—?"

"You *are* in an inquisitional vein today, Higgins . . . Who are you? Are you a detective? Scotland Yard! Why, of course . . . !"

"Culture amuses you, you are amused by Business and Crime! My dear Count, how I have misjudged you! You are also, like me, a very religious man!")

(How much time has passed? Am I dreaming inside a dream? Has a paragraph become calcified, the words turned to stone? Doris comes out of the bathroom. I hardly recognize her. Her beauty glows beneath the skin, her beauty numbs my senses, her eyes have become uncatalogued precious stones from some other place, some other time, her body, swathed in a camel-colored cashmere sheath, is a serpent, or the teen-age daughter of a mythological dragon. Her shoes have sharp points, without asking I know, the name flashes on like a neon sign through a London fog: Mary, Queen of Scots . . .

I stand cold and alert as some ancestral recollection of the Tower of London refrigerates the rose-tinted tiles beneath my feet. I am standing on a platform of crude wood beams, to be sold as a slave, or to be beheaded, I do not know, Doris commands, Doris will tell . . .)

(The Count and Higgins are leaving their office on Via Bissolati. (Today is Thursday, March 12, 1964, former President Truman has a sly horse-trader's smile on his lips, "Lady Bird" Johnson smiles with quiet

Washington hostess dignity, the caption under the Paris *Herald Tribune* photograph reads: "Former President Harry Truman and Mrs. Lyndon B. Johnson review an honor guard on their arrival in Athens to attend King Paul's funeral . . .") The Count is to meet Doris at the foot of the Spanish Stairs in forty minutes. The sky again is a greenish-gray, something strange is going on up there in the upper atmosphere, the Romans are walking along the sidewalks with handkerchiefs over their mouths and noses, like winter denizens of Tokyo, a taxi driver helps a lady shop-owner and her green-legged revolutionary-breasted shopgirl assistant load an improbable scattering of cardboard boxes into the back seat of a Fiat 600 taxi, somewhere, according to the shouting newsboy—an old man without teeth or mustache—a strike is going on in the city, government workers or public health employees, the Count looks down at his watch, Higgins is surreptitiously picking his nose and nervously banging his briefcase against his gray-flannel-swathed leg, the Count suggests: "I tell you what . . . I have half an hour or so before my appointment . . . Why don't we stop in at the Palazzo delle Esposizioni for a quick look at the Michelangelo Exposition?"

"Culture and Crime, the Ides of March—"

"What did you say?"

"An excellent idea, this is one of those days when I haven't the slightest urge to go home . . .")

(Today is a day later, and Doris and the Count, after having spent the night together, have returned to the restaurant on the Via Appia Antica, across the street from the entrance to the Catacombs, where two years ago, at the very beginning of this narration, they had dined. Last night Ben Johnson phoned to tell me that M. is well, that in a few days Jimmy Baldwin will be arriving in Rome. Just before dawn a soft gentle rain fell on the city. Whatever has happened in the atmosphere above or in the hearts of men below has happened, some useless violence has been spent, Rome is quiet today and calm. I must buy two new suits to wear in my Lexington Avenue office. The Count had thoughtfully phoned Signor Vinciguerra, the mustached proprietor of the restaurant, asking him to light a generous fire in the fireplace. The fireplace is an enormous *bocca infernale*, which is what my wife's Aunt Maria said last night at dinner Sophia Loren has. Doris is standing in front of the fireplace with the plastic-covered menu in her hand. The Count looks at his watch and tries not to sigh. In a matter of hours he will be leaving Rome for his new job in Hong Kong, he is sad . . .)

(In the restaurant on the Via Appia Antica across from the Catacombs, the cook is preparing the meal for Doris and the Count. The cook is a plump red-faced woman with blue blinking eyes and a constant expression of whistling irritation on her lips. With the thick wooden spoon she stirs the pasta in the gurgling boiling water with a steady rhythm of controlled violence. She is annoyed that the Count and the Moorish girl have appeared in the restaurant an hour and a half before the normal noon tourist meal. Her fiancé of fifteen years, an even fatter red-faced man with sparse curly black hair, a part-time dealer in illegal archaeological objects, dug up in the vicinity and sold at a very low price to a cleaning woman in a nearby convent, is sitting in a chair by the stove, his battered black hat covering his crotch, reading aloud the day's news from the Sunday, March 15, 1964, edition of *L'Unità*, the organ of the Italian Communist Party. He reads well, he has been educated very recently in an experimental adult education literacy project, his voice is vibrant, the words separate one from the other, creating a strange theatrical effect in the steamy high-ceilinged kitchen of that restaurant on the Via Appia Antica, across from the San Calisto Catacombs, as if some pre-Christian catechism were taking place.

" 'A Billion Dollars loaned to Italy by the USA . . .' "

"What do you bet it's some kind of trick?"

"Be quiet and let me read what it says: 'The United States have conceded to Italy a loan amounting to about a billion dollars, equivalent to 624 miliardi of lire . . .' "

"Better if we got the money from Germany or France, American money is Jewish money, nothing but paper . . ."

"Quiet, you Fascist slut!"

"And quiet you, you gullible Communist pig! Believing everything you read in the papers!"

" 'Electric chair for Jack Ruby—' "

"What a barbarous people, those idiot Americans! Think they can buy up the whole world, then go around killing innocent people on the electric chair!"

"What do you mean, 'innocent'? You saw him kill that Oswald yourself on TV!"

"Who believes what they see on TV! I'm no gullible Communist idiot like you! I don't go around believing everything people want me to believe!"

"If you ask me, you don't believe anything, that's the trouble with you women! You think everyone is sneaky and sly like the Lord made you women—"

"Ha! Ha! Now just listen to this Communist pig, this big fat atheist, talking about the Lord! I suppose for you Khrushchev is the Heavenly Father!"

"Stop spitting in that pot! I know that man out there. He's been here before with that pretty brown girl. He's a Count!"

"Well, you know what you can do with your Count, and what you can do with that Khrushchev Heavenly Father of yours—!"

" 'Dallas, March 14 . . . Capital punishment to be executed on the electric chair: this is the sentence inflicted on Jack Ruby, judged guilty of premeditated homicide by the twelve members of the jury of Dallas . . .' "

"Kill them all, that's what I say! There's not a single one of you men worth the attention of an honest hard-working woman! Huhm! Hand me that salt! Flowers on your graves, that's the most any of you are worth! Even Mussolini, with a fine wife like that, sniffing around that—! Huhm! As far as I'm concerned you can all go to Hell!)

(From the *New York Herald Tribune*, Paris, Monday, March 16: ". . . The government announced last night that Italy, struggling in serious economic difficulties, had obtained $1,225,000,000 in credits from the United States, European central banks and the International Monetary Fund . . ."

". . . Italian Communist leader Palmiro Togliatti said today that the Chinese Communists may be softening their stand . . ."

". . . Police arrested more than 100 students yesterday during a demonstration outside the shop of a barber who has refused to cut Negroes' hair . . ."

". . . Citizens of Dallas, deeply disturbed by a cycle of historic violence in their city, disagreed today over Jack Ruby's condemnation to death. His lawyers, meantime, expressed fears for his life before the verdict can be appealed . . ."

". . . Fear, like an infectious disease, grips a teeming corner of Istanbul. This is the Greek community—about 80,000, and quite prosperous. It feels itself a hostage in the Greek-Turkish confrontation over Cyprus . . ."

". . . When he lands in Mexico City today for a four-day state visit, President De Gaulle of France will get a hero's welcome of a magnitude very near that which President Kennedy enjoyed on his June, 1962, trip . . . Latins are well aware that in the past few years every time the United States and France have gotten nose to nose on an issue, General De Gaulle has boldly done the tweaking. He recognized Red China, for one thing, a move many Latin nations with an eye toward Peking trade would love to make, too . . ."

". . . Malcolm X last week emerged as an independent

operator in the service of Allah and black nationalism in the United States. Ousted as number two man in the Black Muslim movement, he struck a fresh pose of militancy, urging Negroes to buy guns and form rifle clubs for self-defense . . ."

". . . Senator Long replied: 'Anyone who knows anything about hereditary traits knows that all people are not created equal, they are different. Thomas Jefferson, who wrote that statement in the Declaration of Independence, had approximately 200 slaves. He didn't liberate those slaves . . .' "

". . . Elizabeth Taylor and Richard Burton were married today in a simple ceremony in a Montreal hotel room . . . Today's surprise ceremony culminated the well-publicized romance that began in Rome two years ago during the filming of *Cleopatra*, in which both had starring roles . . .")

(In the restaurant across from the Catacombs, along the ancient Appian Way in Rome, the waiter is putting the finishing touches to the table. Doris and the Count are still standing before the blazing fireplace. Doris is saying: "Well, I guess you might call this our Last Supper, Good Friday and Easter coming so early this year . . ."

The tagliatelle arrive in a big bowl shaped like one half of an egg. Steam rises from the bowl. The Count is skilled as a waiter. High, almost to the level of his evasive blue-eyed gaze, he raises the ten-inch lengths of gleaming hot pasta. He fills Doris' plate almost to overflowing. He spoons up the pool of melted butter at the bottom of the bowl and pours it on the mound of pasta, which looks like the shorn hair of a marble goddess. Steam rises from the plate. There is a whole loaf of bread on the spotless white tablecloth. There are flowers in a vase; they are a pale green, pink, a golden yellow, and have tiny brown spots, the petals are large enough to eat. On the table there is no special knife to cut the bread.

Doris waits thoughtfully while the Count serves himself. She sprinkles the fine-grained cheese over her mountain of steaming shorn hair of a marble goddess. She reaches over and picks up the heavy loaf of country-baked bread, and breaks off a hunk, and thoughtfully begins chewing the thick pebble-brown crust.

There is a fiasco of ruby-red wine which both steal glances at but which neither dares yet touch . . .

"I am going to miss you, Doris . . ." the Count says, as neatly he places the heavy silver serving fork parallel to the oval-shaped bowl.

"Why are they sending you to Hong Kong?"

"Company business. Who knows why anyone is sent anywhere? Have you made up your mind about going back to America?"

"I have a feeling I'm going somewhere. I don't know where. You see, I am alone. Now I am alone . . . I don't have a Company like you . . ."

Doris and the Count now eat, they chew in silence, in unison, both thinking along the twin rails of the very same line of reasoning. From the kitchen, as the silence grows noisy because of their chewing, comes radio music; far too many violins . . .

Then suddenly Doris stops chewing and reaches for the fiasco of ruby-red wine, and while doing so, asks in a trembling husky voice: "Raffaele, why don't you take me with you?"

At that moment an enormous bus screeches to a stop outside the restaurant. Moments later a swarm of German or Austrian tourists come pouring in.

"Excuse me, Doris. Yes . . . I think I'll tell you what I was just then thinking. You know what I was thinking. I was just then thinking that it is fun to sin . . ."

"And do you know what *I* was just then thinking?"

"Excuse me if I interrupt—another thought has just popped into my mind: What is the difference between fun and funny? Don't you think there are great political and sociological implications there?"

"Christ! Here we go again! Can't you be serious, not even for a minute?"

"Doris . . . I'm going to Hong Kong, I'm going to miss you, you will not be present in Hong Kong . . ."

"And what makes you so goddamned sure that *you* will be *present* somewhere in the world, that I won't . . . Oh, I forgot, you work for . . . belong to . . . a Company!"

"You make Company sound like 'The Company of——' . . . No, Doris, mine is a commercial airline company . . . They are similar, but not quite the same . . ."

"It's a Company of men, and you're not taking me to Hong Kong with you, so what's the difference?"

"I would take you if I could, but—"

"But . . . ! With you men it's always but, but, but . . . I'm no nun, and here you are stuffing your belly with pasta, about to fly off to Hong Kong and leaving me behind, asking me if I'm going back to America! Well, if you want to know something, I'm going straight—"

"Where, Doris—"

"Back where I came from, that's where I'm going! . . ."

"Then you're going back to America—?"

Several of the Germanic tourists are laughing as only Germanic tourists can laugh on a holiday in Italy. Doris laughs too. The waiter hastens to the Count's table to remove their first-course plates. The waiter apologizes: "Excuse me for abandoning you, but—"

And he nods with an ingratiating smile of complicity toward the foreigners: "The invasion of the barbarians has, as you can well see, begun—"

Perhaps involuntarily, the waiter's glance settles like a fly on Doris' neck . . .

"We ordered roast lamb, I think," the Count says curtly, suddenly annoyed by the waiter's unctuous appeal to racism as a cover-up for his incompetence and inbred servilism . . .

Doris continues to laugh. When the waiter leaves, she says: "The last time we were here, two years ago . . . Do you remember those hunters . . . ?"

"What hunters . . . ?"

"The hunters with shotguns, and muddy boots . . . I never told you, but I had the feeling they were hunting for me . . . But they didn't get me . . . I wonder if they are still alive, those hunters . . ."

"What are you talking about, Doris? Are you sure you feel well?"

"Thank God you're not a writer, thank God you belong to a Company—! You're lucky they're transferring you to Hong Kong . . . Did I tell you my mother married an undertaker?"

"I don't think you've ever talked to me about your mother—"

"I have a mother, you have a mother, all God's children got mommies . . . !"

Again Doris begins laughing. She covers her mouth with her napkin. The Count spills ruby-red wine on the white tablecloth. He forgets to fill Doris' glass. He lights a cigarette. Then as he snuffs out the flame of the match, he realizes his neglect: "Excuse me, *tesoro* . . . !"

Smoke rises, black sulphuric smoke . . .

Suddenly Doris stops laughing. A strange transformation comes over her face. Again her eyes become uncatalogued precious stones. Her voice fades and retires to a musical cave from which, only when the stars are in the correct position, comes the voice of the oracle: "I have a mother, you have a mother, all God's children got mammies . . ."

(And the warm hum of my IBM Executive electric

typewriter abruptly makes a pocket of silence as in an inaudible prayer I add: ". . . for otherwise there is no God!")

But now the long-awaited astral conjunction begins to take place, light years become hours, become days, astrologists, astronomers and human racers take pause, struggle to perceive, impatiently search the skies as the vertical and horizontal hairlines of the Divine Ballistician's gunsight slowly begin to cross, become *the* Cross, Easter Morning's organist sits in Saturn's dying gloom and smiles with the secret bubbling joy of anticipation while practicing a Hallelujah Chorus . . . The black-bandaged beggar woman glances down at her outstretched arthritic hand, reads the tiny crisscrossing lines of humility and greed, the itching tapestry writ on each human child's palm, the palms of monkeys too, she sighs, she coughs, in a scratchy voice the old beggar woman says: "What has happened has happened, what shall take place shall take place, stay afloat, stay afloat, praise be to the Lord of Heaven, the catastrophic reign of Saturn is drawing to an end . . ."

The beggar woman crouches next to a marble horse-trough fountain in Piazza del Popolo, Doris and the Count are crossing the gray polished stones of the ancient Appian Way, they follow behind the gooselike procession of Germanic tourists, headed for the rectangular tufa mouth of the Catacombs, admission fee paid, English-speaking guide assigned, tapers in hand, Doris and the Count are about to go underground, cold deep and narrow the irregular uncomfortable steps that lead to the sacred Underworld of Rome . . .

There is a draft, a presence—the cold flame wavers as . . .

The Count is saying under his breath:

"*I Conti tornano* . . ."

"*I conti tornano?* I don't understand . . ."

"*I conti tornano* . . . In commercial language it means simply that 'the bill is right' . . . Literally, '*I Conti tornano*' means that Counts always return . . ."

" 'I Conti tornano' . . ."

Suddenly now daylight is swallowed up by the phosphorescent glow of darkness, by the powdered bones of all the Saints. Doris and the Count have reached the bottom of the steps. (Is the bottom the top of the triangular law of construction? Where is above? Where is below? Why have the fat-cheeked children played on this their afternoon off? Doris shivers, instinctively she extends her free hand over the flickering flame of her taper. She moves closer to Raffaele so as to touch and be with the alive. Their shoulders touch. Her dangling free hand brushes against his tight flannel-imprisoned organ. (Easter Morning's organist mops his perspiring brow with a tightly woven handkerchief of precious linen and reluctantly heads for home and the ritual bowl of quarreling minestrone . . .) The Count coughs with polite embarrassment. The cheerful young Irish priest, their Orphic guide to this underworld, other world, place, holds up his hand unnecessarily for silence, clears his throat like an amateur tenor in a Dublin bar, and in melodious tones, the melodious tones of the practiced performer, not the tones of the practiced reformer, says: ". . . among the pagan Romans, cremation was the usual method of disposing of the dead, but the early Christians practised inhumation, since this was the custom of the Jews and Jesus himself had been buried in a grave. The Catacombs of Rome are of Christian construction, and were designed from the first as places of sepulture of those who had 'died in the Lord' and in death were not divided from their fellow-believers . . . Reached by stairways, the galleries are some thirty to forty feet below street level, and from ten to fifteen feet high and three feet wide. Innumerable side-galleries branch off from the main corridors . . ."

The Count has never been in the Catacombs before . . . He has never heard these *facts* before. These *facts* were for outlanders, tourists, foreigners, invaders from the South, invaders from the North. Something brushes against the Count's eyes. He blinks. Drops of silver nitrate drop coldly on his closed eyelids. The newborn sees. The Count is suddenly cold, he shivers, he bends toward Doris for the comforting warm contact of her presence.

She is not there. Doris has vanished. The cheerful Irish priest is saying: ". . . On each side of the corridors, horizontal recesses are cut in the wall, one above another. In these, the bodies of the dead were laid, after which they were sealed up with a marble slab or large tiles bearing the names of the deceased. Here and there are small chambers which became chapels in which the Eucharist and the *Agape* or Love Feast were celebrated. The number of separate graves in the Catacombs has been estimated at two million and more, of all races and colors . . ."

The Count walks with desperate calm down the dark cold corridors, shouting silently, his teeth chattering, his fingers clenched, far now from the warm compact circle of English-speaking tourists listening to the spiel of the cheerful young Irish priest guide:

("Doris! . . . Doris! . . . Where are you, Doris? . . . Where are you? . . . Doris! Doris! Where have you gone?")